ROCKET

RAND's Omnibus Calculator of the Kinematics of Earth Trajectories

PRENTICE-HALL SPACE TECHNOLOGY SERIES

C. W. Besserer and Floyd E. Nixon, Editors

ROCKET

RAND's Omnibus Calculator of the Kinematics of Earth Trajectories

BARRY W. BOEHM

The RAND Corporation

PRENTICE-HALL, INC.   ENGLEWOOD CLIFFS, N. J.

PRENTICE-HALL INTERNATIONAL, INC., *London*
PRENTICE-HALL OF AUSTRALIA, PTY., LTD., *Sydney*
PRENTICE-HALL OF CANADA, LTD., *Toronto*
PRENTICE-HALL OF FRANCE, S.A.R.L., *Paris*
PRENTICE-HALL OF INDIA (PRIVATE) LTD., *New Delhi*
PRENTICE-HALL OF JAPAN, INC., *Tokyo*
PRENTICE-HALL DE MEXICO, S.A., *Mexico City*

Printed in the United States of America

C–78202

PREFACE

The conquest of space presents to us a host of difficult problems. How well and how soon we solve these problems will depend greatly on how efficiently we utilize our scarcest and most valuable resource—the ingenuity of the human mind.

The electronic computer offers a possibility of increasing by orders of magnitude the scope and efficiency of our collective thinking operations; indeed such an effect can be seen in the recent history of trajectory computation. Thirty years ago, the computation of a typical trajectory of a projectile involved at least a week of numerical integration by an experienced operator of a desk calculator. A great deal of analytical effort was devoted to the search for integrals to the equations of motion; but although a number of interesting special cases were handled, no general solutions were found.

Today, the computer compresses the week of trajectory computation into seconds, allowing the ingenuity of the erstwhile operator of the desk calculator to concentrate on aspects of the underlying design problem which might otherwise go untouched. Furthermore, the mathematical analyst is now free to devote his talents to the solution of new problems, many of which have been brought into the realm of tractability by the rapid integration capability of the computer— a good example is trajectory optimization.

Of course, it is still necessary to program the computer to integrate the proper trajectory equations. A large number of such programs exist, written for the most part in the language of a particular machine and with reference to the specific purpose—usually performance evaluation of a particular rocket vehicle—for which the program is needed. New needs generally require a new program, involving considerable duplication of effort, or modification of an existing program, a task which is always harder than it looks and which usually involves a sizable expenditure of time and ability.

The advent of FORTRAN as a scientific programming language that can be used on practically all large-scale digital computers makes it possible to contemplate a general trajectory computation program, one which many researchers may use on many different computers without having to spend large amounts of valuable time and ingenuity in adapting the program to their specific needs. The ROCKET program is offered as a candidate for this job.

To be specific, ROCKET—RAND's Omnibus Calculator of the Kinematics of Earth Trajectories—is a digital computer program which mathematically simulates the flight of aerospace vehicles, with the ability to handle flight programs as elaborate as that of a multistage powered vehicle about a rotating oblate planet with a rotating atmosphere. Written in FORTRAN II, it allows a user to specify a vehicle's characteristics and its flight plan, both of which may vary through a wide range of choices, on a set of special-purpose input forms. Throughout its development and refinement, an attempt has been made to keep the ROCKET program as flexible and easy to use as possible.

ROCKET was developed at The RAND Corporation under United States

Air Force Project RAND as an aid to research studies in astronautics and allied fields. In use, it has been found to be a versatile and easily mastered tool, and has been applied in such areas as:

Space booster performance studies;
Tracking network evaluations;
Aerospaceplane design analyses;
Ballistic missile defense investigations;
Advanced aircraft evaluations;
Satellite rendezvous considerations;
ICBM, IRBM, SAM, and ASM performance studies;
Satellite orbit decay predictions;
Heat and mass transfer studies of meteors and re-entry vehicles;
Evaluation of orbit modification techniques;
Verification of aerodynamic characteristics of bodies;
Studies of maneuverability in space;
Evaluation of rocket vehicle guidance schemes;
Aspects of lunar and planetary exploration.

It is the purpose of this manual to acquaint the prospective user with the capabilities and basic theory of the program, and to serve as a reference guide for the researcher using the program. The inclusion of complete descriptions of the input forms and their uses makes it possible to obtain results without recourse to a detailed knowledge of the program's inner workings. Numerous examples provide operational definitions for the various options in the program, and show some of the ways in which ROCKET can be used as a research tool.

A copy of the ROCKET program can be obtained by sending a blank reel of magnetic tape to the SHARE Distribution Agency, IBM Corporation, 112 East Post Road, White Plains, New York.

The development of ROCKET was particularly facilitated by the freedom from pressures afforded by RAND management policies and by the author's opportunity to draw upon the insight and experience of members of the RAND technical staff. Especially valuable were the many stimulating discussions with D. N. Morris and R. T. Oelschlager. Others who furnished or inspired significant improvement include R. T. Gabler, C. Gazley, Jr., E. M. Graef, E. C. Heffern, W. C. Hollis, Herbert Rosenzweig, H. B. Schechter, G. F. Schilling, and W. L. Sibley. It is a pleasure to acknowledge the contributions made by their work and ideas. Also, the program owes a substantial cultural debt to a similar trajectory program developed by H. B. Hilton and his associates at General Dynamics/Astronautics, with which the author was affiliated during the years 1957–59. The original manuscript of the manual has undergone remarkable improvement at the dexterous editorial hands of W. B. Holland, and has been typed with unusual care by Arlene Leppek and Joan Pederson.

CONTENTS

Appendix

FIGURES

TABLES

SYMBOL	PROGRAM SYMBOL	EXPLANATION
a	AEU	Semimajor axis of osculating orbit (Fig. 34) (eru).
$\bar{a}$	ARLP	Acceleration vector $(= \ddot{\bar{r}})$ (ft/sec^2).
a_E	AEFT	Equatorial radius of earth (Fig. 41) (ft).
A,B,Al		Vehicle-oriented axis system (Fig. 12-14).
A_A	AAX	Aerodynamic forces along vehicle axes (lb).
A_B	ABT	
A_{Al}	AAL	
A_E		Exit area of rocket engine (ft^2).
A_N		Normal aerodynamic force (Fig. 36) (lb).
A_{ref}	AREA	Reference area of vehicle (ft^2).
A_3	A3	Ratio, maximum to minimum truncation error.
A_4	A4	Reference number, relative error computation.
b_E	BE	Polar radius of earth (Fig. 41) (ft).

SYMBOL	PROGRAM SYMBOL	EXPLANATION
C_A	CAX	Aerodynamic force coefficients along vehicle axes.
C_B	CBT	
C_{AL}	CAL	
C_{AERO}	CAERO	Modifying coefficient, aerodynamics.
C_{EX}	CEXT	Modifying coefficient, extra.
C_{FF}	CFFL	Modifying coefficient, fuel flow.
C_G	CGUID	Modifying coefficient, guidance.
C_T	CTHR	Modifying coefficient, thrust.
e	ECC	Eccentricity of osculating orbit.
e_E	EECC	Eccentricity of earth ellipsoid.
e_I		Eccentricity of range plane ellipse.
E		Eccentric anomaly of osculating orbit (Fig. 34) (rad).
$\overline{E}$	A2	Maximum relative truncation error for integration.
EGY	EGY	Orbital energy of vehicle per unit mass (ft^2/sec^2).
f_E	FLAT	Flattening of earth ellipsoid.

SYMBOL	PROGRAM SYMBOL	EXPLANATION
$\overline{F}$	FRLP FABAL	Force acting on vehicle (lb).
g_o	GZ	Mass conversion factor (ft/sec^2).
$\overline{G}$		Gravitational acceleration of vehicle (ft/sec^2).
h	HFT	Altitude of vehicle above reference spherical earth (ft).
$\dot{h}$	HD	First derivative of h (ft/sec).
$\ddot{h}$	HDD	Second derivative of h (ft/sec^2).
h_A	HAPØG	Apogee altitude of osculating orbit above spherical earth (Fig. 40) (n mi).
h_E	ALT HEFT	Altitude of vehicle above sea level (ft).
h_{E_T}	AT1 AT2 AT3	Altitude of tracking station above sea level (ft).
h_P		Perigee altitude of osculating orbit above spherical earth (n mi).
i		Inclination of plane of osculating orbit to earth's equator (Fig. 34) (deg).
i_P		Inclination of range plane to earth's equator (Fig. 42) (rad).

SYMBOL	PROGRAM SYMBOL	EXPLANATION
$i_{s,m}$	QISD QIMD	Solar, lunar orbit inclination (Fig. 43) (deg).
I	ERTIA	Vehicle moment of inertia (slug-ft^2).
I_{SP}		Specific impulse of rocket engine (sec).
J_E	EJ	Second harmonic component of earth's gravitational potential.
$\overline{K}$	XZ,YZ,ZZ	Earth-referenced launch vector (Fig. 39, 42) (ft).
$\overline{K}_I$	XZI,YZI, ZZI	Inertial launch vector (ft).
m		Mass of vehicle (slug).
M	EMACH	Mach number (ratio of earth-referenced velocity to local speed of sound).
$\overline{M}$		Vehicle subsurface point (Fig. 40, 42).
M_1		
M_2		Rotation matrices.
M_3		
$\overline{N}$		Normal to range plane (Fig. 42) or to orbital plane.

SYMBOL	PROGRAM SYMBOL	EXPLANATION
P		Semi-latus rectum of osculating orbit (Fig. 34) (ft).
P_A	APRES	Atmospheric pressure (lb/ft^2).
P_{SL}	SLPRES	Atmospheric pressure at sea level (lb/ft^2).
q	Q	Dynamic pressure (lb/ft^2).
$\bar{q}$		Arbitrary vector.
$\bar{r}$	RXYZG XYZI	Vehicle position vector from center of earth (Fig. 10, 34, 44) (ft).
r	RFT	Distance of vehicle from center of earth (ft).
r_o	RZFT	Radius of spherical earth model (ft).
	RZNM	Radius of spherical earth model (n mi).
$r_{s,m}$	RRS RRM	Solar, lunar orbital radius (ft).
R, L, P		Vehicle position-oriented axis system (Fig. 10, 13, 39).
R_G	RGAS	Gas constant ($\frac{ft\text{-}lb}{slug\text{-}^\circ R}$).
R_{IMP}	RIMP	Surface range from launch point to vacuum ballistic impact point (Fig. 40) (n mi).

SYMBOL	PROGRAM SYMBOL	EXPLANATION
R_S	RANGE	Surface range from launch point to vehicle subsurface point (Fig. 40, 42) (n mi)
R_{S1}	RWS	Slant range from launch point to vehicle (Fig. 40) (ft)
R_T	RT	Distance from tracking station to center of earth (ft).
t	TIME	Time (sec).
t_H	TIMP	Time at extrapolated impact (sec).
t_Z	TZ	Time at which initial conditions specified (sec).
T	THRUST	Total thrust force (Fig. 35) (lb).
T_A	TAX	Thrust forces along vehicle axes (Fig. 35) (lb).
T_B	TBT	
T_{A1}	TAL	
T_{air}		Local air temperature ($^{\circ}$R).
u		Argument of latitude of osculating orbit (Fig. 34) (deg).
$\overline{V}$	VRLP	Vehicle velocity vector (Fig. 13, 14, 36) (ft/sec).
v_A		Inertial velocity at apogee of osculating orbit (ft/sec).

SYMBOL	PROGRAM SYMBOL	EXPLANATION
v_C		Circular velocity at apogee of osculating orbit (ft/sec).
v_E	VE VELE	Earth-referenced velocity (ft/sec).
v_I	VI	Inertial velocity (ft/sec).
v_P		True anomaly of osculating orbit (Fig. 34) (deg).
v_S	VSND	Local speed of sound (ft/sec).
V,S,N		Velocity-oriented axis system (Fig. 13, 14).
w	WGT	Weight of vehicle (lb).
$\dot{w}$	WD	Weight derivative (lb/sec).
w_{FC}	WFC	Final vehicle weight in circular orbit (lb).
w_J	WJETT	Jettison weight (lb).
$\bar{x}$		Vehicle state vector.
x_G, y_G, z_G		Earth-referenced axis system (Fig. 10, 39).
x_I, y_I, z_I		Inertial reference axis system (Fig. 10, 11, 43).
x_T, y_T, z_T		Tracker-oriented axis system (Fig. 32, 33).
x_ρ, y_ρ, z_ρ		Tracker-to-vehicle oriented axis system (Fig. 33).
X_A	XAX	Extra nongravitational forces along vehicle axes (lb).
X_B	XBT	
X_{A1}	XAL	

SYMBOL	PROGRAM SYMBOL	EXPLANATION
X_{CG}	XCG	Distance from nose to center of gravity of vehicle (Fig. 38) (ft).
X_{CP}	XCP	Distance from nose to center of pressure of vehicle (Fig. 38) (ft).
X_{HL}	XHL	Distance from nose to hinge line of vehicle (Fig. 38) (ft).
α	ALPHAD	Angle of attack (Fig. 13, 14, 36, 37) (deg).
	ALPHAR	Angle of attack (Fig. 13, 14, 36, 37) (rad).
α_T	ALPHTD	Total angle of attack (Fig. 36) (deg).
β	BETAD	Sideslip angle (Fig. 13, 14, 36) (deg).
	BETAR	Sideslip angle (Fig. 13, 14, 36) (rad).
β_A	BTAIR	Exponential atmosphere decay factor (ft^{-1}),
γ	GAMMAD	Flight path angle between earth-referenced velocity vector and local horizontal (p. 157) (Fig. 13, 14, 37) (deg).
	GAMMAR	Flight path angle between earth-referenced velocity vector and local horizontal (p. 157) (Fig. 13, 14, 37) (rad).
γ_A	GAMAIR	Ratio of specific heats of air.

SYMBOL	PROGRAM SYMBOL	EXPLANATION
γ_H	GIMP	Inertial flight path angle at extrapolated impact (deg).
γ_I	GAMID	Inertial flight path angle between inertial velocity vector and local horizontal (p. 157) (deg).
$\Delta a_{s,m}$	DFS DFM	Solar, lunar acceleration of vehicle relative to earth (ft/sec^2).
Δ_E	DELER	Central angle between earth-referenced launch point and vehicle position vector (Fig. 39) (rad).
Δ_I	DELIR	Central angle between inertial launch point and vehicle position vector (Fig. 37) (rad).
Δt	DTIME	Integration stepsize (sec).
Δt_{max}	A5	Maximum stepsize (sec).
Δt_{min}	A6	Minimum stepsize (sec).
Δt_{PO}	DTPϕ	Output interval (sec).
Δv_D	DVDR	Velocity loss due to drag (ft/sec).
Δv_G	DVGR	Velocity loss due to gravity (ft/sec).
Θ	THETAD	Attitude angle between vehicle's A-axis and local horizontal (Fig. 37) (deg).

SYMBOL	PROGRAM SYMBOL	EXPLANATION
Θ_A	TAD	Azimuth angle measured eastward from tracker north-pointing vector to projection of tracker-to-vehicle vector onto tracker local horizontal (Fig. 33) (deg).
Θ_E	TED	Elevation angle of tracker-to-vehicle vector above tracker local horizontal (Fig. 33) (deg).
Θ_I	THETIR	Inertial attitude angle between vehicle's A-axis and inertial launch horizontal (Fig. 37) (rad).
Θ_R	THRG	Range angle from vehicle to extrapolated impact point (Fig. 40) (rad).
$\Theta_{s,m}$	THS THM	Solar, lunar position angle (Fig. 43) (rad).
Θ_T	TILT	Tilt angle (Fig. 24) (deg).
$(\Theta_o)_{s,m}$	TOSD TOMD	Solar, lunar initial position angle (Fig. 43) (deg).
λ	ELϕNR	Earth longitude of vehicle, measured eastward from Greenwich prime meridian (Fig. 10, 39) (rad).
$\dot{\lambda}$	ELD	First derivative of λ (rad/sec).

SYMBOL	PROGRAM SYMBOL	EXPLANATION
$\ddot{\lambda}$	ELDD	Second derivative of λ $(\text{rad}/\text{sec}^2)$.
λ_{G_o}	ELGZD	Inertial longitude of Greenwich prime meridian at $t = o$ (Fig. 10) (deg).
λ_H	ELHD	Earth longitude at extrapolated impact (deg).
λ_I	ELI	Inertial longitude of vehicle (Fig. 10, 11) (rad).
λ_K	ELØNZ	Earth longitude of launch point (Fig. 39) (deg).
λ_P		Earth longitude of intersection of equator and range plane (Fig. 42) (rad).
μ	EMU	Earth gravitational constant $(\text{ft}^3/\text{sec}^2)$.
$\mu_{s,m}$	EMUS EMUM	Solar, lunar gravitational constant $(\text{ft}^3/\text{sec}^2)$.
ν_L		Central angle between equator and launch point in range plane (Fig. 42) (rad).
ν_M		Central angle between equator and vehicle sub-surface point in range plane (Fig. 42) (rad).
ρ_A	ADENS	Air density $(\text{slug}/\text{ft}^3)$.
ρ_{SL}	SLDENS	Air density at sea level $(\text{slug}/\text{ft}^3)$.

SYMBOL	PROGRAM SYMBOL	EXPLANATION
ρ_T	RHϕ	Distance from tracker to vehicle (Fig. 33) (ft).
σ_B		Bank angle of vehicle (deg).
σ_R	SIGR	Effective roll angle of vehicle (Fig. 36) (rad).
τ_α	TAUAL	Thrust deflection angle toward A1-axis (Fig. 35) (deg).
τ_β	TAUBT	Thrust deflection angle toward B-axis (Fig. 35) (deg).
ϕ	PHIR	Geocentric latitude of vehicle (Fig. 10, 39, 41) (rad).
$\dot{\phi}$	PHD	First derivative of ϕ (rad/sec).
$\ddot{\phi}$	PHDD	Second derivative of ϕ (rad/sec^2).
ϕ_{GD}	PHIRGD	Geodetic latitude of vehicle (Fig. 41) (rad).
ϕ_H	PHHD	Geocentric latitude at extrapolated impact (deg).
ϕ_K	PHIZR	Geocentric latitude of launch point (Fig. 39) (rad).
ϕ_T	PT1 PT2 PT3	Latitude of tracker (deg).

SYMBOL	PROGRAM SYMBOL	EXPLANATION
Ψ_V	PSIVD	Azimuth angle measured eastward from vehicle local north-pointing vector to projection of velocity vector onto local horizontal (Fig. 13, 14) (deg).
	PSIVR	Azimuth angle measured eastward from vehicle local north-pointing vector to projection of velocity vector onto local horizontal (Fig. 13, 14) (rad).
ω	WE	Earth rotation rate (rad/sec).
ω_P		Angle between ascending node and perigee of osculating orbit, in orbital plane (Fig. 34) (deg).
$\omega_{s,m}$	WWS WWM	Solar, lunar angular velocity (rad/sec).
Ω		Inertial longitude of ascending node of osculating orbit (Fig. 34) (deg).
$\Omega_{s,m}$	ϕMSD ϕMMD	Solar, lunar longitude of ascending node (Fig. 43) (deg).
$\overline{I}_R, \overline{I}_L, \overline{I}_P$		Unit vectors in R, L, P directions (Fig. 10, 11).
$\overline{I}_{x_I}, \overline{I}_{y_I}, \overline{I}_{z_I}$		Unit vectors in x_I, y_I, z_I directions (Fig. 10, 11).

Chapter 1

INTRODUCTION

A. GENERAL REMARKS

A rocket flight into space is an expensive and
hazardous venture requiring a great deal of experimentation and the solution of many complex problems: How should
one design a rocket vehicle to carry a man to the moon and
back? Would an orbital rendezvous scheme help? Is it
better to use liquid, solid, electrical, or nuclear propulsion for the upper stages? What sort of midcourse
guidance is required?

To try to answer such questions by constructing and
flying various types of rocket vehicles would be extremely
expensive. Fortunately, much of the experimentation can
be conducted without having to employ large numbers of
trained men to make and control intricate configurations
of rocket hardware. It happens, conveniently, that the
part of the universe which concerns the gross behavior
of rocket vehicles can be quite adequately approximated
by a mathematical model. Even more convenient is the fact
that the model need consist only of finite sequences of
algebraic operations upon rational numbers, since operations of this nature are suited for rapid and reliable
execution by a modern digital computer. Thus, a computer
program incorporating the appropriate model can approximate the behavior of a rocket at far less cost in terms

of time, money, and effort than that required by a test flight.

Although the computer model is by no means a complete substitute for the physical system, its value lies mainly in its contribution to the performance of a physical rocket vehicle with respect to a desired mission. This contribution stems from the ability of the computer model to pre-evaluate the relative performance of proposed vehicle designs, to point out and investigate critical parts of the flight, and to provide a proving ground for ideas to improve performance.

The ROCKET program contains such a model. It creates a sub-universe in which a "mathematical astronaut," pro-vided with a digital computer, a deck of punched cards, and an input form, can chart voyages and direct vehicles through the reaches of terrestrial and interplanetary space, voyages which take seconds rather than hours or weeks.

There are a number of computer models which produce the same sort of results that the ROCKET program does, often in a more extensive and elegant manner. One dis-tinguishing feature of the ROCKET program is that, to our knowledge, it is the only general trajectory program which allows the researcher to obtain his results without recourse to a detailed knowledge of the inner workings of the program. It is not necessary to find, or train, or become a programmer with a mastery of the internal logic of the program, to get results.

People with little programming experience, and with only a modest knowledge of rocketry, have found the following preparation sufficient for setting up ROCKET runs:

1. Reading the expository material in Chaps. 1-3;

2. Skimming the reference material in Chap. 5 and the Appendices;

3. Studying, fairly carefully, the examples in Chap. 4, referring throughout to the relevant material in the Appendices.

With this much preparation, it should be possible to set up any trajectory problem which can be expressed in terms of the existing ROCKET model.

In addition, a working knowledge of FORTRAN will enable the user to write subroutines which extend the model into areas of his choice. Another distinguishing feature of the program is that such subroutines can be fitted into its framework in a simple and natural manner, allowing the user to devote his ingenuity to the formulation of his model rather than to figuring out how to fit it into the main program.

B. SCOPE OF THE ROCKET PROGRAM

The title of the program, ROCKET, is an acronym which was derived in the usual way by selecting an interesting contraction and then hunting for words to fit it. The longer title, "RAND's Omnibus Calculator of the Kinematics of Earth Trajectories," does, however, give an idea of the general-purpose nature of the program. The program is able to simulate the flight of space boosters, ICBMs, IRBMs, boost-glide vehicles, satellites, re-entry vehicles, airplanes, torpedoes, or any hybrids thereof, with approximately equal facility, for operation in the vicinity of an earth which is either fixed or rotating, spherical or oblate; or in the vicinity of other planets, such as Mars or Venus. The vehicle may be made to travel through any atmosphere or hydrosphere that the user can describe by means of tables of geophysical parameters; axial and normal aerodynamic coefficients and forces may be specified in any one of a number of ways. A great variety of options is also available for the specification of propulsive forces and guidance programs.

The program allows three translational and three rotational degrees of freedom. Initial conditions may be specified at any point on, above, or below the surface of the earth (or central body), with any initial velocity and vehicle orientation. The program may be run forward or backward in time from the initial conditions.

In general, the assumption is made that all forces acting on the vehicle are applied at its center of gravity. The program does contain a set of routines which provide an elementary capability for determining vehicle attitude

from the moments about the center of gravity. However,
as the program would probably not be very efficient in
simulating a detailed autopilot loop or in calculating the
associated vehicle structural loads or bending dynamics,
those effects have not been included.

The ROCKET program not only traces the trajectory of
the vehicle as a function of time, but also provides detailed information on its performance during flight. The
program can print, at the user's option, statements of
the aerodynamic forces, propulsion components, aerodynamic
heating rates, guidance quantities, tracking coordinates
and rates for as many as three tracking stations, and
instantaneous osculating orbital elements; it can be
modified easily to print any other special quantities a
user may find desirable.

The program has been designed to be able to investigate a number of variations on a given trajectory in a
single run, greatly simplifying the process of trajectory
matching or of making parameter studies. Another tool
which has been provided is a recursive scheme by which one
may reach a desired set of end conditions by iteration on
a set of control parameters.

Above all, ROCKET has been designed with as much
flexibility and growth potential as possible without com-
promising its computational speed and ease of use. The
effects which are enumerated in this Manual represent only

a small fraction of those which the program can handle. Thus, no matter how extraordinary a configuration or flight plan one has, there is a good probability that a reasonable facsimile of it can be simulated by the ROCKET program. Indeed, a very sophisticated user might view the program simply as a convenient reference framework in which to program and experiment with detailed simulations of those particular rocket phenomena of interest to him.

However, one must be aware of the perils of over-identification. A perfect flight through the mathematical sub-universe does not guarantee that the corresponding flight through the physical universe will be perfect. Great care must be taken to assess the interactions of the flight quantities computed in the model with those factors, relevant to a physical flight, which have been neglected in the construction of the model.

The finer details, such as the effects of acceleration stresses upon human passengers or the effects of temperature variations on guidance equipment, cannot all be incorporated into a computer model, although they can be of critical importance in an actual flight. Thus, a user of the model must attain and maintain an awareness of danger areas, or combinations of flight quantities which may jeopardize the vehicle's mission by their effect upon components which have been assumed to work perfectly throughout the flight.

C. THE METHOD OF TRAJECTORY COMPUTATION

The physical basis of the ROCKET model is embodied in Newton's second law, $\overline{F} = m\overline{a}$.[*] If we identify $\overline{a}$ with the second derivative $\ddot{\overline{r}}$ of the position vector $\overline{r}$ of a rocket vehicle, and if we are furnished with the initial position $\overline{r}_o$ and velocity $\dot{\overline{r}}_o$ of the vehicle at a time t_o, plus a means of computing at any time t the force $\overline{F}$ acting at the center of gravity of the rocket as a function of t, $\overline{r}$, and $\dot{\overline{r}}$, we may then set up the following scheme for tracing the trajectory of the vehicle. (A trajectory can be thought of as a record of the vehicle's position vector $\overline{r}$ as a function of time.) Certain simplifying assumptions, such as constant mass and step-function integrands, are made here to clarify the exposition. They are not made in the program.

1a. Compute $\overline{F}\, (t_o,\, \overline{r}_o,\, \dot{\overline{r}}_o)$

1b. Compute $\ddot{\overline{r}} = \overline{F}/m$

1c. Integrate to find $\dot{\overline{r}}_1 = \dot{\overline{r}}_o + \int_{t_o}^{t_1} \ddot{\overline{r}}\; dt$

1d. Integrate to find $\overline{r}_1 = \overline{r}_o + \int_{t_o}^{t_1} \dot{\overline{r}}\; dt$

2a. Compute $\overline{F}\, (t_1,\, \overline{r}_1,\, \dot{\overline{r}}_1)$

2b. Compute $\ddot{\overline{r}} = \overline{F}/m$

2c. Integrate to find $\dot{\overline{r}}_2 = \dot{\overline{r}}_1 + \int_{t_1}^{t_2} \ddot{\overline{r}}\; dt$

---

[*]Where $\overline{F}$ is the vector force applied at the center of gravity of a body of mass m, and $\overline{a}$ is the resulting acceleration.

2d. Integrate to find $\overline{r}_2 = \overline{r}_1 + \int\limits_{t_1}^{t_2} \dot{\overline{r}}\ dt$

3a. Compute $\overline{F}\ (t_2,\ \overline{r}_2,\ \dot{\overline{r}}_2)$

etc.

The repetitive nature of this scheme suggests that it may be formed into a loop, a structure well suited to processing by a stored-program digital computer. The kernel of the ROCKET program is formed by a loop of this nature; it is sketched out in flowchart form below. The constant-mass assumption has been dropped, but the treatment of the integrand is still simplified.

Most of the desired flight patterns for rocket vehicles require that more than one means of specifying the magnitude and orientation of the force vector $\overline{F}$ be used during the vehicle's flight. To take a simple example, in an elementary one-stage vertical sounding rocket, there are two distinct sections of its trajectory, during which the forces acting on the vehicle are quite different in nature. In the first section, a propulsive force acts positively along the vehicle axis and an aerodynamic force acts negatively along the axis; in the second section, after the rocket engine has burned out, the aerodynamic force is the only nongravitational force acting on the vehicle. The method of computing $\overline{F}$ changes considerably from section to section, even in this example; in simulations involving more complicated flight patterns, there may be a considerable number of discontinuities in the specification of $\overline{F}$.

For this reason a ROCKET trajectory is processed in consecutive sections, each using as initial conditions in its integration loop the end conditions of the previous section, and each requiring a separate statement from the user of the program as to how he wishes to specify the force vector $\overline{F}$ as a function of t, w, $\overline{r}$, and $\dot{\overline{r}}$; and how long he

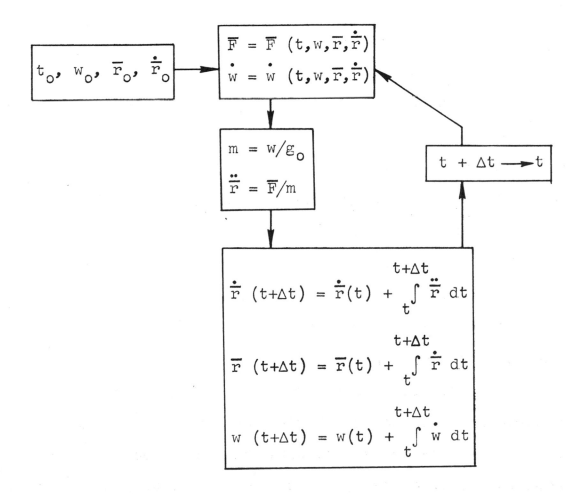

ROCKET: Basic Integration Loop

wishes this particular specification to hold before switching to another section and a different means of computing $\bar{F}$. The means by which the user communicates these specifications to the ROCKET program are outlined briefly in the next section.

D. COMMUNICATION WITH THE PROGRAM

In this introductory chapter we are trying to look at the ROCKET program in a number of different ways, in an attempt to communicate as much of a feel for the program as possible. We can characterize the ROCKET program as: a mathematical sub-universe, as in Sec. A; a black box producing various kinds of outputs as a function of its inputs, as in Sec. B; or a numerical integrator of a particular set of differential equations, as in Sec. C. In this, the concluding section, we look at it as a group of logical and computational components, organized so that they can be used together easily and simply to perform a desired service--i.e., computing a particular trajectory--out of a large class of similar services.

Components common to practically all users, such as the computation of gravitational accelerations and resolution of force components, are automatically used by the program without the user having to worry about them. Components such as those providing for the effects of earth rotation or oblateness, or for the computation and printing of related sets of output quantities, have been coded into the program but are used only if a switch provided on a specially designed input form has been set by the user.

Finally, each section of a ROCKET trajectory has a place into which a user may plug in, by means of a FORTRAN CALL statement entered into a standardized subroutine known as a flight program for the section, any of a number of available component subroutines which compute quantities of interest along the trajectory, including the calculation of the magnitudes and directions of the nongravitational forces affecting the course of the user's simulated vehicle. In addition, a user of the ROCKET program can write his own subroutine and plug it in via the flight program; if it follows a few simple rules of consistency, it will work when called upon.

Communication: Input Forms and Outline of Chapters

The basic input form for the ROCKET program is shown in Figs. 1 and 2 (at 80% of actual size); the form presently used is printed on both sides of a single sheet of $8\frac{1}{2}$x11 paper. Only the first four of the twenty available sections are provided for on these forms; sections 5-20 can be handled similarly, however. The part shown in Fig. 1 is called the Flight Control Form. On this form the user enters a number of control parameters which specify how the trajectory begins (initial time, weight, position, and velocity), how long each section of the trajectory will last, what sort of earth model is desired, what to print

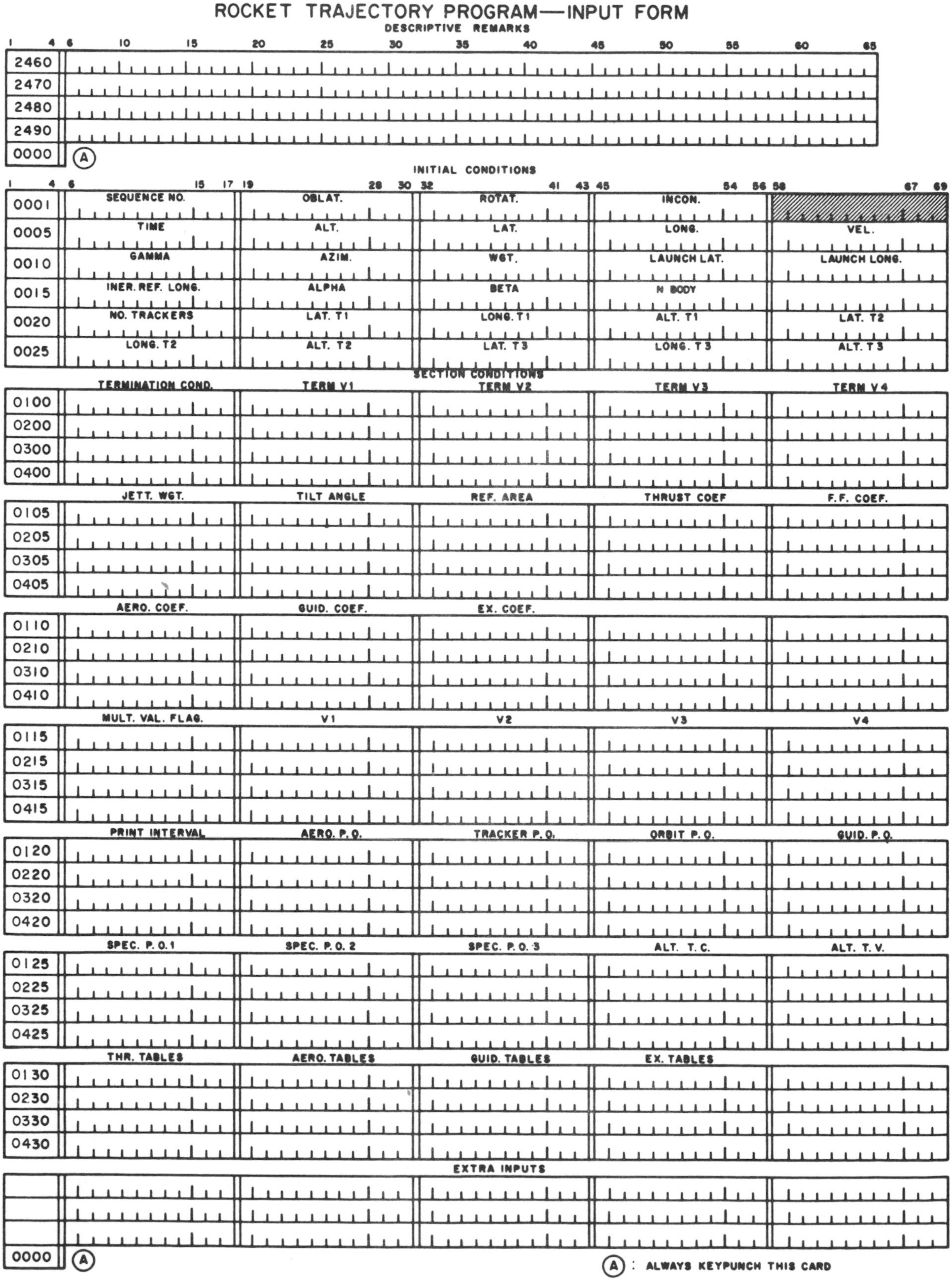

ROCKET TRAJECTORY PROGRAM—INPUT FORM

DESCRIPTIVE REMARKS

1 4 6 10 15 20 25 30 35 40 45 50 55 60 65

2460
2470
2480
2490
0000 (A)

INITIAL CONDITIONS

1 4 6 15 17 19 28 30 32 41 43 45 54 56 58 67 69

0001	SEQUENCE NO.	OBLAT.	ROTAT.	INCON.	
0005	TIME	ALT.	LAT.	LONG.	VEL.
0010	GAMMA	AZIM.	WGT.	LAUNCH LAT.	LAUNCH LONG.
0015	INER. REF. LONG.	ALPHA	BETA	N BODY	
0020	NO. TRACKERS	LAT. T1	LONG. T1	ALT. T1	LAT. T2
0025	LONG. T2	ALT. T2	LAT. T3	LONG. T3	ALT. T3

SECTION CONDITIONS

	TERMINATION COND.	TERM V1	TERM V2	TERM V3	TERM V4
0100					
0200					
0300					
0400					
	JETT. WGT.	TILT ANGLE	REF. AREA	THRUST COEF	F.F. COEF.
0105					
0205					
0305					
0405					
	AERO. COEF.	GUID. COEF.	EX. COEF.		
0110					
0210					
0310					
0410					
	MULT. VAL. FLAG.	V1	V2	V3	V4
0115					
0215					
0315					
0415					
	PRINT INTERVAL	AERO. P.O.	TRACKER P.O.	ORBIT P.O.	GUID. P.O.
0120					
0220					
0320					
0420					
	SPEC. P.O.1	SPEC. P.O.2	SPEC. P.O.3	ALT. T.C.	ALT. T.V.
0125					
0225					
0325					
0425					
	THR. TABLES	AERO. TABLES	GUID. TABLES	EX. TABLES	
0130					
0230					
0330					
0430					

EXTRA INPUTS

0000 (A)

(A) : ALWAYS KEYPUNCH THIS CARD

Fig. 1- ROCKET Flight Control Form

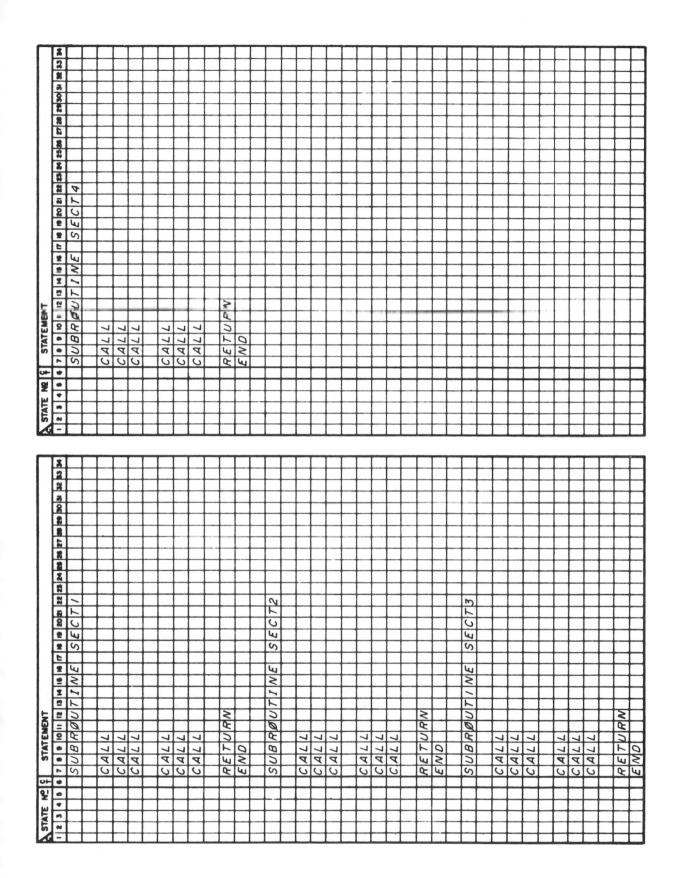

Fig. 2- ROCKET Flight Programming Form

out and how often to do so, and whether or not to use a
number of optional features which are included in the program. Generally, most of these entries can be left blank.

The basic aspects and techniques of flight control
are discussed in Chap. 2, and a detailed explanation of
each entry on the Flight Control Form is given in Appendix A.

Figure 2 displays the Flight Programming Form. On
this form the user provides, for each section of the
trajectory, a sequence of references to those computational subroutines which are needed to specify the force
vector $\bar{F}$ acting on the vehicle as a function of the time
t, vehicle weight w, position $\bar{r}$, and velocity $\dot{\bar{r}}$, in the
desired manner. Only the nongravitational components of
$\bar{F}$ need be computed by these subroutines. This sequence
of references, in the form of FORTRAN CALL statements, is
called the section's flight program. The flight program
usually determines the nongravitational components of the
force vector $\bar{F}$ acting on a vehicle by computing the forces
acting along the vehicle's three body axes and producing
two angles which relate the body axes to the earth-referenced
system in which the integrations are carried out. Chapter
3 contains an explanation of the elements of flight programming; detailed descriptions of the computational subroutines
available to the flight program are given in Appendix B.

Another set of input forms, shown in Figs. 3 and 4,

ROCKET ONE-DIMENSIONAL TABLE

2995	TABLE NO.	STAGE	NO. ENTRIES	
0000	BASE LOC.	NO. DER VAR.	CYCLE	USE ONLY IF TABLE NO. = 0

0000	COMMENTS

INDEPENDENT VARIABLE

0000
0005
0010
0015
0020
0025
0030
0035
0040
0045
0050
0055
0060
0065
0070

FIRST DEPENDENT VARIABLE

0000
0005
0010
0015
0020
0025
0030
0035
0040
0045
0050
0055
0060
0065
0070

SECOND DEPENDENT VARIABLE

0000
0005
0010
0015
0020
0025
0030
0035
0040
0045
0050
0055
0060
0065
0070

Fig. 3- Input Form: One-Demensional Tables

ROCKET TWO-DIMENSIONAL TABLE

2995	TABLE NO. +17 / +02	STAGE +1 / +01	NO. ENTRIES 1 +11 / +02	NO. ENTRIES 2 +5 / +01	
0000	BASE LOC.	NO. DER. VAR.	CYCLE 1	CYCLE 2	USE ONLY IF TABLE NO. = 0

0000	NORMAL AERO. FORCE COEFF -- SAMPLE TWO-DIMENSIONAL TABLE

FIRST INDEPENDENT VARIABLE

0000	+9 / +00	+5 / +00	+8 / +00	+9 / +00	+1 / +01
0005	+11 / +01	+12 / +01	+15 / +01	+2 / +01	+5 / +01
0010	+3 / +02				
0015					
0020					

SECOND INDEPENDENT VARIABLE

0000	+0 / +00	+1 / +01	+2 / +01	+5 / +01	+5 / +02
0005					

DEPENDENT VARIABLE 1 (OR 6)

0000	+0 / +00	+0 / +00	+0 / +00	+9 / +00	+0 / +00
0005	+0 / +00	+0 / +00	+9 / +00	+0 / +00	+0 / +00
0010	+9 / +00				
0015					
0020					

DEPENDENT VARIABLE 2 (OR 7)

0000	+4 / -01	+42 / -01	+46 / -01	+5 / -01	+55 / -01
0005	+6 / -01	+52 / -01	+44 / -01	+36 / -01	+31 / -01
0010	+3 / -01				
0015					
0020					

DEPENDENT VARIABLE 3 (OR 8)

0000	+65 / -01	+67 / -01	+7 / -01	+75 / -01	+82 / -01
0005	+9 / -01	+8 / -01	+7 / -01	+6 / -01	+52 / -01
0010	+5 / -01				
0015					
0020					

DEPENDENT VARIABLE 4 (OR 9)

0000	+12 / +00	+124 / +00	+13 / +00	+138 / +00	+148 / +00
0005	+6 / +00	+142 / +00	+125 / +00	+112 / +00	+192 / +00
0010	+1 / +00				
0015					
0020					

DEPENDENT VARIABLE 5 (OR 10)

0000	+7 / +00	+71 / +00	+72 / +00	+74 / +00	+76 / +00
0005	+8 / +00	+75 / +00	+7 / +00	+65 / +00	+6 / +00
0010	+6 / +00				
0015					
0020					

Fig. 4- Input Form: Two-Dimensional Tables

is sometimes necessary for communications with the program.
These forms are used to express, by means of tables,
simple or complicated mathematical functions whose use may
be necessary to describe the environment of a rocket in
flight. A basic outline of the tables and their uses is
given in Chap. 3, Sec. E; detailed specifications are
given in Appendix C.

In Chap. 4, a number of illustrative examples are
presented which take hypothetical trajectory problems and
show in detail the steps which a user would take in determining what sort of trajectories the ROCKET program
could produce in order to contribute toward solution of
the problems. They also show how one would prepare the
necessary input forms to communicate to the program the
information it needs to be able to run the desired trajectories.

Communication with the program also includes the program's output to the user. The frequency and quantity of
output is controlled by the user via the flight control
form. A basic set of trajectory quantities is always
printed; several other sets are available, representing
detailed aerodynamic, guidance, orbital, or tracking information, and are printed only at the express desire of
the user. Provision has also been made to print out
quantities not included in these standard categories.
Chapter 5 contains examples and explanations of the various
output quantities.

Further information required by a user to communicate intelligently with the program is supplied by Appendix D, which describes the various environmental models of the earth and solar system; and Appendix E, which discusses some of the operational aspects of the program: speed, accuracy, capabilities and limitations, and programming characteristics.

Finally, an index is supplied to facilitate the search for particular bits of information. Also, full scale copies of the Flight Control Form and the Flight Programming Form have been placed at the end of the Manual, following the Indexes. These can be detached and used for reference while reading the Manual, which refers to them continually, or used to duplicate copies of the forms for use with the program.

In order to avert possible misunderstandings, it should be mentioned that the words "ROCKET program" always refer to the digital computer program, and not to any operational program involving physical rockets.

Chapter 2

FLIGHT CONTROL

In order to provide the reader with a frame of reference for assimilation of the material to follow, an outline of the logical design of the ROCKET program is given in terms of the flowchart shown in Fig. 5. In a sense, flight control consists of setting up entries on the input form which will determine the course of the program through the network depicted by the flowchart. Output flags channel the program into the output routines at the proper times, termination conditions derail the program out of the integration loop into the next branch or section of the trajectory, further section or run inputs assure the program it has more work to do and send it back into action again. Most of the details of flight control are discussed in Appendix A, which presents a complete explanation of each entry on the Flight Control Form. The succeeding sections of this chapter treat the more general aspects of controlling ROCKET flights.

A. NATURE OF INPUT TO THE PROGRAM

By looking at the ROCKET basic flowchart, and utilizing the knowledge that the program is a standard one with respect to the FORTRAN system, we can get an idea of the order in which the program accepts input.

Fig.5- ROCKET Program Basic Flowchart

First, the flight programs and any other supplementary subroutines written in FORTRAN source language are compiled. Next, the binary ROCKET program deck is read in, preceded by any additional binary decks (these can include, of course, decks from previously compiled flight programs or supplementary subroutines). Input data is then read in, alphabetic data first, followed by numerical data, including tables, initial conditions, and control parameters. The program then runs the trajectory or set of trajectories determined by the flight programs and the set of input data, and returns to see if any further variations are desired. If so, it reads in whatever variations in input data are furnished and proceeds to run trajectories based on the modified input data, again returning for more variations and terminating only when no further variations are given.

Table I shows the order in which input is presented to the program. The order follows that of the flight control form, with the additional fact that tables are inserted directly behind the first "0000" card of each run.

Table I

ORDER OF INPUT

1. Data for First Run

    a. Comments

    b. A card with "0000" in columns 1-4

    c. Tables

    d. Initial Conditions

    e. Section Conditions

    f. A card with "0000" in columns 1-4

2. Data for Second Run

    a. Comments differing from those of first run

    b. A card with "0000" in columns 1-4

    c. Tables differing from those of first run

    d. Initial Conditions differing from those of first run

    e. Section Conditions differing from those of first run

    f. A card with "0000" in columns 1-4

3. Data for Third Run

    a. Comments differing from those of second run

    b. A card with "0000" in columns 1-4

    c.

B. RUNS, SECTIONS, AND BRANCHES

As has been implied in the previous section, the unit of trajectory processing between successive returns to read in more data is called a run; generally, as may be seen by the two "0000" cards which are always punched on the flight control part of the input form (Fig. 1), a run corresponds to the processing of one input form.

For example, suppose that, after one run has been completed, we wish to run a variant upon it. We take a second input form, fill out only those quantities which will differ from their counterparts in the first run, and place it behind the first. If our first input form describes the flight of a space booster with a launch weight of 400,000 lbs, and we wish to see what would happen to its trajectory if the launch weight were increased to 420,000 lbs, leaving all other flight parameters unchanged, our second Flight Control Form would have 420,000 in the weight slot (0012) and the rest of its entries blank.

A run is divided into sections, which can be thought of as intervals of continuity in the trajectory differential equations. A transition between one section and the next usually implies a breakpoint in the means by which the force vector is calculated; perhaps by the introduction of a new flight program with different ways of obtaining forces or orientation angles; perhaps by a change in tables; or perhaps by the introduction of a single discontinuity such as the instantaneous jettisoning of some of the vehicle's mass. However, one can change sections for other reasons, such as to change the frequency of output. Input for each section consists of a flight program (described in Chap. 3) and a number of control constants, called Section Conditions, which are entered by means of the Flight Control Form (see Appendix A, Sec. 2). As many as twenty sections can be accommodated in a single run. The first two digits of an entry in the Section Conditions correspond to the number of the section; thus, 0320 specifies the print interval during the third section of a run.

The ROCKET program has the ability to sit astride several parallel time tracks, as it were, and compute what might happen to a trajectory had a number of different possible courses been followed during its history. Parallel trajectories formed in this manner are called branches. By the use of branches, variations in later sections of a run may be investigated without having to run the whole trajectory over and duplicate the earlier stages. Figure 6 shows a possible ICBM-type run plotted in the range-altitude plane, with four sections and eventually four branches. In this run the first two sections--a vertical lift-off and an initial pitch-over program--have a single branch. During Section 3, two branches are established in order to investigate, say, a variation in the guidance program

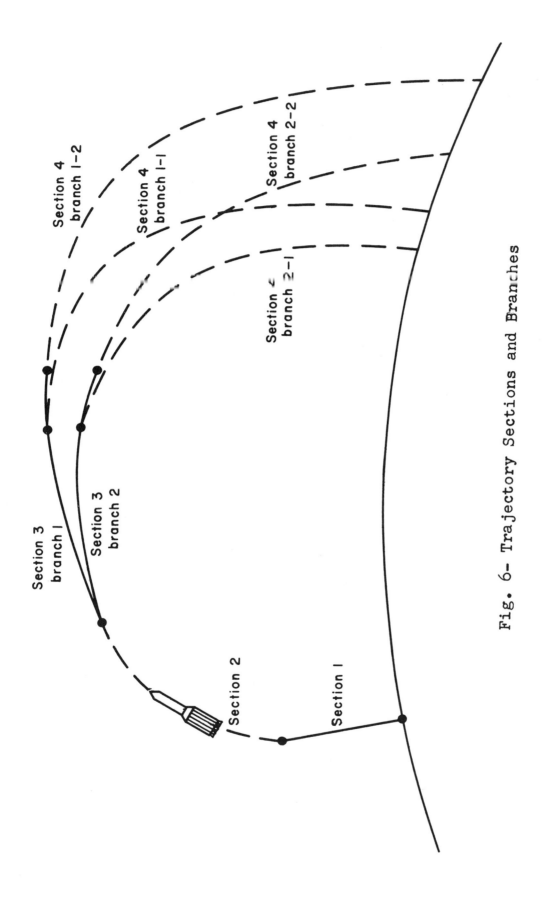

Fig. 6- Trajectory Sections and Branches

The four branches in Section 4, a ballistic coast phase, represent a variation in the time of termination of Section 3, compounded with the original guidance variation.

A section may contain up to thirty-six branches, making an extremely large amount of investigation of variations possible within a single run. Great care must be taken in using this feature, however, because a mistake made in setting up one of the earlier sections of a trajectory means a waste of a great deal of computer time in computing the fates of its then worthless progeny.

C.   TERMINATION OF A SECTION

A section is terminated when a selected flight parameter reaches a desired value. The flight parameter is selected from the list given in Table II by placing the table item number of the desired parameter in the TERM. COND. slot (location --00 in the Section Conditions on the **Flight Control Form**). ROCKET integrates until the selected parameter passes the termination value, and then interpolates to find the time at which the parameter would be equal to the termination value. A linear interpolation will be made if the integer in the TERM. COND. slot has a positive sign; a parabolic interpolation if the integer in the TERM. COND. slot has a negative sign.

Table II

TERMINATION CONDITIONS

Item No.	Program Symbol	Quantity
1	TIME	time t (sec)
2	WGT	weight w (lb)
3	ALT	height above sea level h_E (ft)
4	VELE	earth-referenced velocity v_E (ft/sec)
5	RANGE	surface range R_S (n mi)
6	Q	dynamic pressure q (lb/ft^2)
7	GAMMAD	flight path angle γ (deg)
8	AXCEL	axial acceleration (g's)
9	PSIVD	velocity azimuth angle Ψ_v (deg)
10	HAPØG	ballistic apogee altitude h_A (n mi)
11	RIMP	ballistic impact range R_{IMP} (n mi)
12	VI	inertial velocity v_I (ft/sec)
13	GAMID	inertial flight path angle γ_I (deg)
14	RWS	slant range R_{S1} (ft)
15	HD	radial velocity $\dot{h}$ (ft/sec)
16	ALPHAD	angle of attack α (deg)
17	THETAD	attitude angle Θ (deg)

Thus, if the number -5. appears in the TERM. COND. slot, the program will integrate until the time t_p, at which the surface range R_S passes its termination value; then will conduct a parabolic interpolation to find the time t_s, at which R_S equals the termination value. It will then integrate the trajectory back to the time t_s, at which point it terminates the section or branch.

Some care must be taken that the termination quantity is being properly furnished to the program; this precaution is explained on page 59.

Additional variables can be added to the list of termination quantities by a simple modification of one of the program subroutines (GETTC).

Multiple Termination Values

The locations TERM. V1 through TERM. V4 (--01 through --04 in the Section Conditions on the Flight Control Form) are provided for the specification of up to four termination values. Nominally, only the first one is used. The others can be used to investigate the effects of variation of the termination value; they will result in the branching process described above.

For example, if along with a TERM. COND. of -5., we have TERM. V1 = 10., and TERM. V2 = 15., ROCKET will find the point at which R_S = 10 n mi (by parabolic interpolation), store the quantities necessary for a later restart, then proceed along in the same section until it finds the point at which R_S = 15 n mi, at which it also stores the quantities necessary for a restart. The next termination value, TERM. V3, is zero, which the program interprets as the signal that the last value has been processed; ROCKET then proceeds, if there are no more branches in this section, to the next section, where it will first process the branch starting at R_S = 10 n mi, then return and process the branch starting at R_S = 15 n mi.

Alternate Termination Condition

An alternate termination condition and associated termination value (ALT. T.C. and ALT. T.V.; locations --28 and --29 in the Section Conditions) are available to the user. They operate in the same manner as they would if they were the regular termination condition and value, except that once the alternate value has been reached, the branch is terminated, no matter how many termination values in the regular list have not been reached. If all the values in the regular list are reached before the alternate value, the branch is terminated without proceeding to the alternate value.

Referring to our previous example, suppose we have also ALT. T.C. = 3. and ALT. T.V. = 5000. If the vehicle reaches an altitude of 5000 ft before reaching a range of 10 n mi, the branch will be terminated at the point, located by linear interpolation, at which h_E = 5000 ft (see Fig. 7). If the vehicle reaches

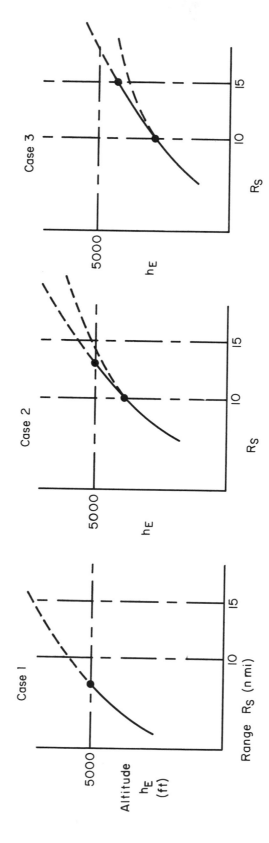

Fig. 7 - Alternate Termination Condition

h_E = 5000 ft after reaching R_S = 10 n mi, but before reaching R_S = 15 n mi, two branches, one at R_S = 10 n mi and one at h_E = 5000 ft, will issue from the original branch. If the vehicle reaches R_S = 15 n mi before reaching h_E = 5000 ft, two branches will also ensue, one at R_S = 10 n mi, the other at R_S = 15 n mi.

Two "backup" termination conditions have been built into the program to stop possible runaway trajectories:

1. Vehicle weight becoming zero or negative;

2. Vehicle altitude h_E falling below a certain altitude (nominally 1000 ft below sea level).

D. BRANCHING

The basic idea of branching is explained in Sec. B, and a means of branching by multiple termination values has been treated in Sec. C. The type of branching of major interest in investigating trajectory variations is that stemming from the use of the MULT. VAL. FLAG (location --15 in the Section Conditions) and the four associated values, V1-V4 (locations --16 through --19).

To use this feature, the last two digits of its location in the Section Conditions on the Flight Control Form (i.e., the location modulo 100; also given in Appendix A, Sec. 2) of the section condition being multiplexed, is placed as a positive floating point integer into the MULT. VAL. FLAG slot, and the

multiple values are placed into as many of the slots
V1, V2, V3, V4 as are needed. For each branch in the
section, ROCKET then takes each value in turn, identifies
it as the appropriate section condition, and integrates
up to the termination condition (or conditions), creating
a branch (or number of branches) each time, until it
either completes four multiple values or comes to a zero
value, at which point it terminates the branch.

For example, suppose we wish to look at the effect
of variations in a rocket engine's specific impulse
during a section of the trajectory, while keeping the
fuel flow fixed. In this particular section we would
put the integer +8. (the location modulo 100 of the THRUST
COEF. slot on the Flight Control Form; see p. 132) in the
MULT. VAL. FLAG slot, and the values 0.9, 1.0, and 1.1
into V1, V2, and V3. When ROCKET came to this section,
it would first place the value 0.9 in the THRUST COEF. slot
and then run through the section, multiplying the thrust
throughout by 0.9, the value of the thrust coefficient C_T.
It would then store the quantities necessary for a later
restart and proceed similarly through the section twice
more from the beginning, using the values 1.0 and 1.1 as
thrust multipliers. When it returned again and found V4
= 0, it would terminate the section and proceed to propa-
gate the three branches in the next section. Figure 8
shows the three resulting branches.

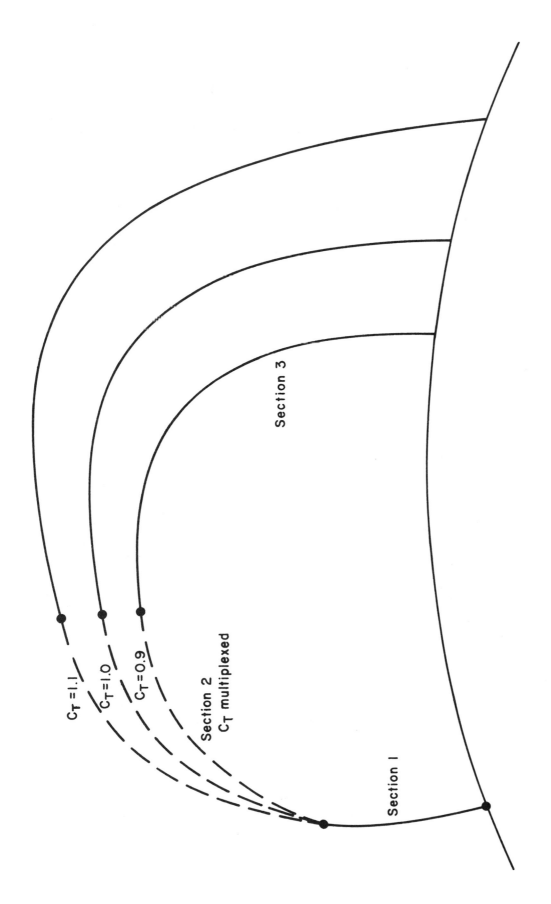

Fig. 8- The Branching Process

E. ITERATION

If it is desired to meet more than one condition at
the end of a section, ROCKET has the capability of iter-
ating on an end condition. To use this option, a negative
number is placed in the MULT. VAL. FLAG slot (--15 in the
Section Conditions). ROCKET will then transfer control
at the end of the section to a subroutine called ITER8,
which is provided by the user and tells ROCKET either that
the end condition is satisfactory, in which case ITER8 places
a 1. in a cell called THRU, or that it is not, in which
case ITER8 adjusts the section conditions in a way designed
to improve the outcome and has ROCKET run the section over
again. If six iterations are executed without obtaining
convergence, ROCKET terminates the section and proceeds,
using the values obtained at the end of the sixth iteration.

For example, suppose we wish to reach an altitude h_E
of 100,000 ft ($\pm$ 100 ft) at the end of a section, and we
know that by changing the guidance coefficient C_G by 0.1
units we change the end altitude by approximately 1000
ft. This information is programmed into a subroutine
called ITER8, entering the section with an initial value
of C_G = 1., a number which we know is a good initial
guess. If this choice results, say, in an end altitude
of 105,000 ft, ITER8 will say, "This is not good enough,"
decrease C_G by .05 units, and have ROCKET run the section
again with C_G = .95. Suppose this time the end altitude

is 99,800 ft. ITER8 elects to try again, increasing
C_G by .002, and has ROCKET run the section a third time
with C_G = .952. If this produces an end altitude of
99,980 ft, ITER8 will see that this is within the 100-ft
tolerance and place a 1. in THRU. ROCKET will then infer
that the iteration has converged and proceed to the next
section. Figure 9 illustrates the process.

The four entries V1-V4 can in this case be used to
supply information such as desired values, initial guesses,
and partial derivatives, to the ITER8 subroutine. The
program symbols for these entries are EMV(1), EMV(2),
EMV(3), and EMV(4).

The sample ITER8 subroutine below can be used for
the above example or for any variations on it involving
different end altitudes, tolerances, or partial deriva-
tives $\frac{\partial C_G}{\partial h_E}$. Such a subroutine can be entered onto the
extra lines available on the Flight Programming Form.

```
       SUBROUTINE ITER8
       (COMMON Package)
       DH = HEFT - EMV(1)
       IF (ABSF(DH) - EMV(2))  1,1,2
   1   THRU = 1.
       GO TO 3
   2   DCG = DH * EMV(3)
       CGUID = CGUID + DCG
   3   RETURN
       END
```

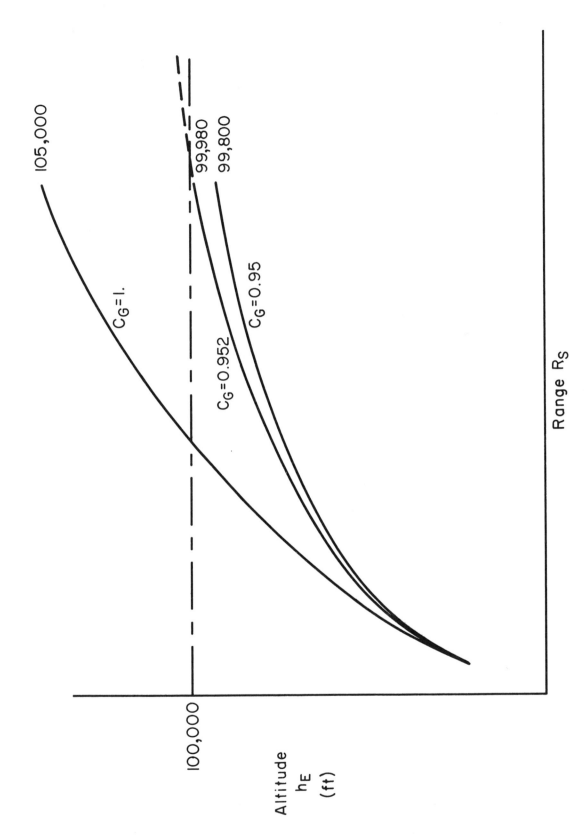

Fig. 9— Iteration on End Condition

Comments:

COMMON package: explained in Appendix E, Sec. 5.

HEFT, CGUID: program symbols for h_E, C_G obtained from List of Symbols.

EMV(1): refers to end altitude. For the example above, 100,000 would be placed in the section's V1 slot (--16).

EMV(2): refers to tolerance. For the example above, 100 would be placed in the section's V2 slot (--17).

EMB(3): refers to partial derivative $\frac{\partial C_G}{\partial h_E}$. For the example above, 0.1 would be placed in the section's V3 slot (--18).

Simple Maximization and Minimization

An iterative subroutine is available which finds, to within a certain degree of relative accuracy, the value of a section condition X, within an interval $[X_L, X_U]$, which produces a maximum or minimum of a quantity of interest Y evaluated at the end of the section. This subroutine is activated by placing a negative number in the MULT. VAL. FLAG slot of the section, and using an ITER8 subroutine of the following form:

```
SUBRØUTINE ITER8
(COMMON package)
CALL FIBITR (X,Y,XM)
```

```
            RETURN

            END
```

where X and Y stand for the program symbols of the variables of interest, defined via the COMMON package (Appendix E, Sec. 5); and XM is +1. if a maximum is being sought, or -1. if a minimum is being sought. The lower bound X_L is entered in the normal place for X on the Flight Control Form, and the upper bound X_U is entered in the section's V1 slot.

The subroutine FIBITR then conducts an approximate Fibonaccian search for the extremum of Y. The Fibonaccian search has been shown[1] to minimize the number of calculations of Y necessary to locate the extremum to any degree of accuracy. Eight passes through the section are taken, after which the maximizing value of X is known to within $.056(X_U-X_L)$. At this point FIBITR places a 1. in THRU, allowing ROCKET to proceed to the next section.

This subroutine is guaranteed to work only if Y(X) is a unimodal function on the interval $[X_L,X_U]$; i.e., if there exists a point X_0 in the interval such that Y(X) is strictly increasing on one side of X_0 and strictly decreasing on the other side. Strictly convex and concave functions are unimodal.

Example

Suppose we know that the altitude of a vehicle at the end of a section reaches a maximum for some choice of the guidance coefficient C_G between 1.5 and 2.0, and we wish to run a trajectory with approximately that choice of C_G which produces the maximum altitude at the end of the section. We would place a -1. in the section's MULT. VAL. FLAG slot, a 1.5 in the GUID. COEF. slot, a 2.0 in the V1 slot, and we would use the statement

CALL FIBITR (CGUID, HEFT, +1.)

in the ITER8 subroutine. ROCKET would then run the section eight times, ending up with a maximizing value of C_G accurate to within 0.028, and then proceed to the next section using the end conditions produced by the maximizing C_G.

Another example of this technique is given as Example 4 in Chap. 4.

Chapter 3
FLIGHT PROGRAMMING

On the left-hand side, toward the bottom, of the
ROCKET program basic flowchart shown in Fig. 5 (p. 20) is
a double-bordered box with the notation "Compute Forces,
Angles." This is the function performed by the flight
program. At each integration step along the trajectory,
ROCKET transfers control of the machine to the flight
program of the current section. This flight program is a
small FORTRAN subroutine consisting usually of CALL
statements referring to various computational subroutines
in the ROCKET library, which will compute, as a function
of the current position and velocity of the vehicle, the
nongravitational forces acting along the three axes of
the vehicle and the angles relating these axes to the
local coordinate system, plus any other quantities of
interest to the user. After these quantities have been
computed, control of the machine is transferred back to
the main program, which then resolves the forces into the
local coordinate system, converts them into accelerations
and adds the accelerations due to gravity, and integrates
the resultant accelerations to find the vehicle's velocity
and position at the next point along the trajectory.

Before going into a more thorough explanation of how
to put together a flight program which will calculate

forces and angles in the right way, as we shall do in Sec. C below, it is necessary to go into a bit of detail to introduce some of the coordinate systems, state vectors, and orientation angles commonly used by the program. In doing so, in Sections A and B, we shall also present the elements of a simple derivation of the equations of motion used by the program, and set down some of the more important relationships between the program variables.

A. COORDINATE SYSTEMS AND EQUATIONS OF MOTION

Suppose we have, as in Fig. 10, an inertial rectangular coordinate system with origin at the earth's center, a unit vector $\bar{I}_{x_I}$ directed toward the intersection of the earth's equator with the meridian of zero inertial longitude (usually taken in the direction of the vernal equinox), a unit vector $\bar{I}_{z_I}$ pointing to the north pole, and a unit vector $\bar{I}_{y_I}$ directed so as to form a right-handed system. Suppose also that at time t we have a vector $\bar{r}$ defined in spherical coordinates by its distance from the earth's center r, its geocentric latitude ϕ, and its inertial longitude λ_I.

The longitude λ of the vector $\bar{r}$ with respect to the earth-referenced Greenwich prime meridian is related to the inertial longitude at time t by

$$\lambda_I = \lambda + \lambda_{G_o} + \omega t, \qquad (3-1)$$

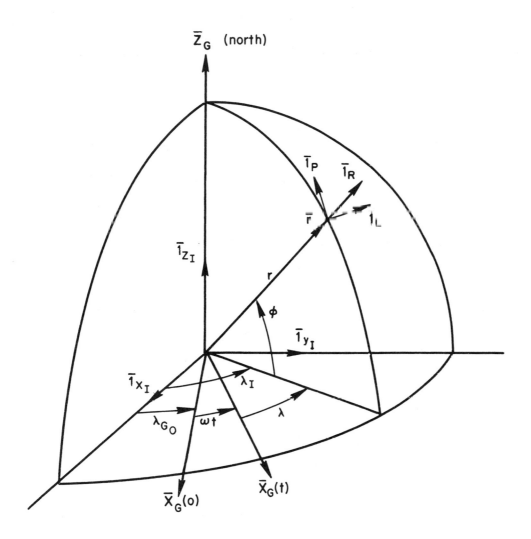

Fig. 10- Inertial and Local Coordinates

where λ_{G_o} is the inertial longitude of the Greenwich meridian at t = 0, and ω is the angular rate of the earth's eastward rotation (see Fig. 10). The vector $\overline{x}_G$ lies in the equatorial plane in the direction of the Greenwich meridian and, with $\overline{z}_G$, is the basis of an earth-referenced system to be used later.

At present, we wish to derive an expression for the acceleration of the vector $\overline{r}$ in terms of a rotating earth-referenced coordinate system with a unit vector $\overline{I}_R$ directed radially away from the earth's center, a unit vector $\overline{I}_L$ directed eastward along the local parallel of latitude, and a unit vector $\overline{I}_P$ directed northward along the local meridian of earth longitude.

In the inertial (x_I, y_I, z_I) system, the acceleration is expressed simply as

$$\overline{a} = \ddot{\overline{r}} = \ddot{r}_{x_I} \overline{I}_{x_I} + \ddot{r}_{y_I} \overline{I}_{y_I} + \ddot{r}_{z_I} \overline{I}_{z_I} \, . \qquad (3\text{-}2)$$

We can express the (x_I, y_I, z_I) components of an arbitrary vector $\overline{Q}$ in terms of its (R, L, P) components by means of the rotation matrix $M_1(\lambda_I, \phi)$.

$$\begin{pmatrix} Q_{x_I} \\ Q_{y_I} \\ Q_{z_I} \end{pmatrix} = M_1(\lambda_I, \phi) \begin{pmatrix} Q_R \\ Q_L \\ Q_P \end{pmatrix} , \text{ or } M_1^{-1}(\lambda_{I_1} \phi) \begin{pmatrix} Q_{x_I} \\ Q_{y_I} \\ Q_{z_I} \end{pmatrix} = \begin{pmatrix} Q_R \\ Q_L \\ Q_P \end{pmatrix} ,$$

where

$$M_1(\lambda_I,\phi) = \begin{pmatrix} \cos\phi\cos\lambda_I & -\sin\lambda_I & -\sin\phi\cos\lambda_I \\ \cos\phi\sin\lambda_I & \cos\lambda_I & -\sin\phi\sin\lambda_I \\ \sin\phi & 0 & \cos\phi \end{pmatrix}, \quad (3\text{-}3)$$

and $M_1^{-1}(\lambda_{I_1}\phi)$ is the inverse matrix to M_1, or in this case (since M_1 is orthonormal), the transpose of M_1. To look at the transformation in another way, the elements of M_1 are the partial derivatives $\frac{\partial Q_{x_I}}{\partial Q_R}$, $\frac{\partial Q_{x_I}}{\partial Q_L}$, etc., and the matrix equation can be thought of as an application of the chain rule for partial differentiation:

$$Q_{x_I} = \frac{\partial Q_{x_I}}{\partial Q_R} Q_R + \frac{\partial Q_{x_I}}{\partial Q_L} Q_L + \frac{\partial Q_{x_I}}{\partial Q_P} Q_P,$$

with similar expressions for Q_{y_I} and Q_{z_I}. In Fig. 11 we have translated the (R,L,P) system to the earth's center for easier visualization of the transformation.

We may then use the matrix M_1^{-1} to transform the (x_I,y_I,z_I) components of $\ddot{\bar{r}}$ into its (R,L,P) components. Eq. (3-2) then takes the form:

$$\bar{a} = \bar{I}_R \left(\ddot{r}_{x_I} \cos\phi\cos\lambda_I + \ddot{r}_{y_I} \cos\phi\sin\lambda_I + \ddot{r}_{z_I} \sin\phi \right)$$

$$+ \bar{I}_L \left(-\ddot{r}_{x_I}\sin\lambda_I + \ddot{r}_{y_I}\cos\lambda_I + \ddot{r}_{z_I}(0) \right)$$

$$+ \bar{I}_P \left(-\ddot{r}_{x_I}\sin\phi\cos\lambda_I - \ddot{r}_{y_I}\sin\phi\sin\lambda_I + \ddot{r}_{z_I}\cos\phi \right).$$

$$(3\text{-}4)$$

-46-

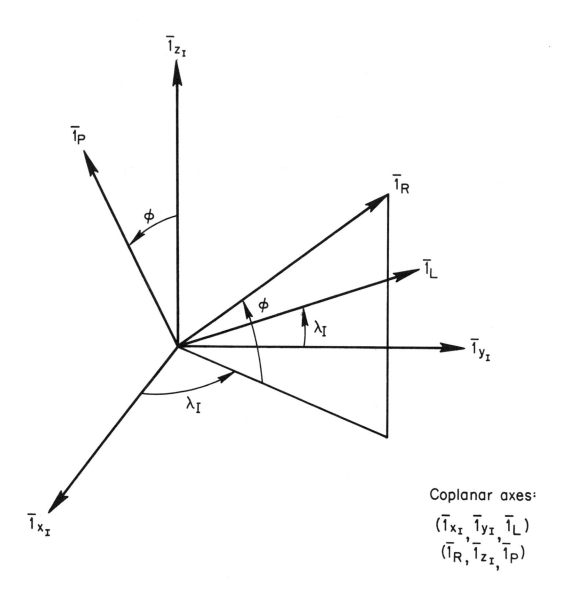

Coplanar axes:
$$(\overline{1}_{x_I}, \overline{1}_{y_I}, \overline{1}_L)$$
$$(\overline{1}_R, \overline{1}_{z_I}, \overline{1}_P)$$

Fig. 11- Inertial-to-Local Coordinate Rotations

We now note from Fig. 10 (p. 43) that

$$r_{x_I} = r \cos \phi \cos (\lambda + \lambda_{G_o} + \omega t)$$

$$r_{y_I} = r \cos \phi \sin (\lambda + \lambda_{G_o} + \omega t) \qquad (3\text{-}5)$$

$$r_{z_I} = r \sin \phi.$$

If we twice differentiate these expressions for r_{x_I}, r_{y_I}, and r_{z_I}, and substitute the resulting $\ddot{r}_{x_I}$, $\ddot{r}_{y_I}$, and $\ddot{r}_{z_I}$ into Eq. (3-4), we obtain, after some manipulation,

$$\bar{a} = \bar{I}_R (\ddot{r} - r\dot{\phi}^2 - r (\dot{\lambda} + \omega)^2 \cos^2 \phi)$$

$$+ \bar{I}_L (\ddot{\lambda} r \cos \phi + 2\dot{r} (\dot{\lambda} + \omega) \cos \phi - 2r\dot{\phi} (\dot{\lambda} + \omega) \sin \phi)$$

$$+ \bar{I}_p (\ddot{\phi} r + r (\dot{\lambda} + \omega)^2 \sin \phi \cos \phi + 2\dot{r}\dot{\phi}). \qquad (3\text{-}6)$$

Equating the components of this vector equation and making the substitution $\bar{a} = \bar{F}/m$ gives us the following set of equations of motion:

$$\ddot{r} = F_R/m + r\dot{\phi}^2 + r (\dot{\lambda} + \omega)^2 \cos^2 \phi$$

$$\ddot{\lambda} = [F_L/m - 2\dot{r} (\dot{\lambda} + \omega) \cos \phi + 2r\dot{\phi} (\dot{\lambda} + \omega) \sin \phi]/r \cos \phi$$

$$\ddot{\phi} = [F_p/m - r (\dot{\lambda} + \omega)^2 \sin \phi \cos \phi - 2\dot{r}\dot{\phi}]/r. \qquad (3\text{-}7)$$

We now have a system of second order differential
equations in the variables r, λ, ϕ, representing radial
distance, earth longitude, and geocentric latitude. This
is the system used by the ROCKET program;* it computes
the mass flow rate and the forces acting on a vehicle
as a function of the time t and the vehicle's position
$\bar{r}$ and velocity $\dot{\bar{r}}$, and resolves them into the components
F_R, F_L, F_P, which it then uses to compute the second
derivatives $\ddot{r}$, $\ddot{\lambda}$, $\ddot{\phi}$ by Eq. (3-7). ROCKET then numerically
integrates through at time Δt to obtain the mass of the
vehicle, its position components r, λ, ϕ, and the first
derivatives $\dot{r}$, $\dot{\lambda}$, $\dot{\phi}$ (the velocity components) at a
time t + Δt. With the new time, position, velocity, and
mass, it computes the resulting accelerations and begins
the process anew, as indicated by the flow diagram on
page 9.

B. RESOLUTION OF FORCE COMPONENTS

The forces calculated by a user's flight program are
most conveniently resolved along the vehicle's body axes.
These are shown in Fig. 12: in airplane parlance, the
A-axis points out the nose of the vehicle; the B-axis, the

---

*With one slight difference: to minimize round-off
errors, ROCKET uses the height above a reference sphere,
h = r - r_o, instead of r. Since r_o is a constant
(the mean radius of the earth), we have $\dot{h}=\dot{r}$, $\ddot{h}=\ddot{r}$.

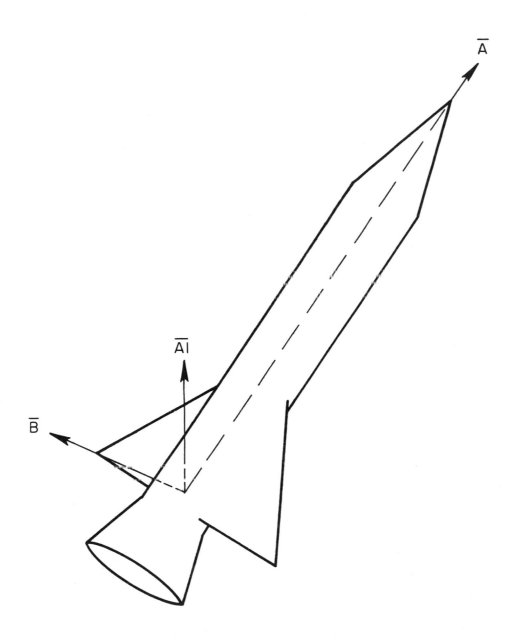

Fig. 12- Vehicle-Oriented Axes

left wing tip; and the Al-axis, the top of the cockpit.
As the A-axis points along the main body axis of the
vehicle, components along this axis are sometimes called,
with no great loss of clarity, axial forces.

Besides calculating the forces acting along the body
axes of the vehicle, the flight program must also furnish
the information necessary to relate the body axes to the
(R, L, P) system in which the integration is carried out.
It does this by specifying two angles, α and β, physically
known as the vehicle angle of attack and sideslip angle,
respectively. These angles relate the (A, B, Al) system of
body axes to a (V, S, N) system based on the velocity
vector. The (V, S, N) system is related to the (R, L, P) system by the flight path angle γ (defined as the angle between the velocity vector $\overline{V}$, and the local horizontal;
i.e., the plane formed by the L- and P-axes), and the
velocity azimuth angle Ψ_v. The situation is depicted in
Figs. 13 and 14; Fig. 13 shows the combined relationship,
and Fig. 14 shows separately the two stages of the transition. The rotation matrices necessary to transform the
vehicle-oriented force vector (F_A, F_B, F_{Al}) into the
earth-referenced force vector (F_R, F_L, F_P) are given
below:

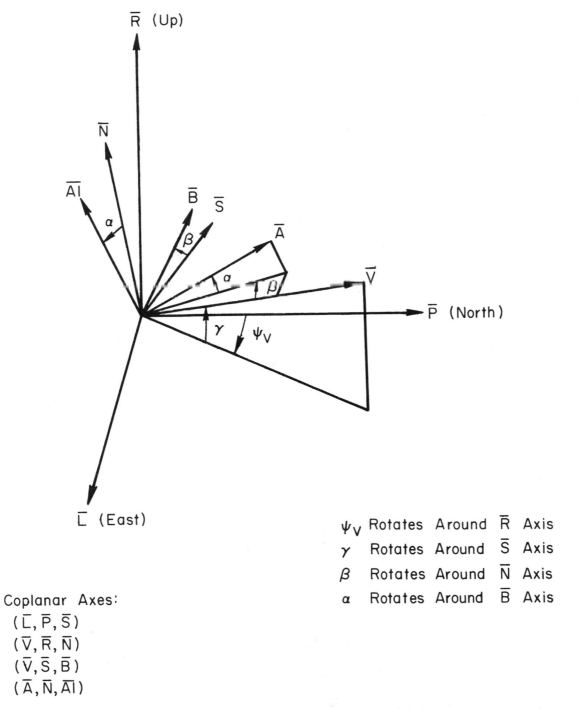

Coplanar Axes:
 $(\bar{L}, \bar{P}, \bar{S})$
 $(\bar{V}, \bar{R}, \bar{N})$
 $(\bar{V}, \bar{S}, \bar{B})$
 $(\bar{A}, \bar{N}, \overline{Al})$

ψ_V Rotates Around $\bar{R}$ Axis
γ Rotates Around $\bar{S}$ Axis
β Rotates Around $\bar{N}$ Axis
α Rotates Around $\bar{B}$ Axis

Fig. 13- Local and Vehicle Coordinates

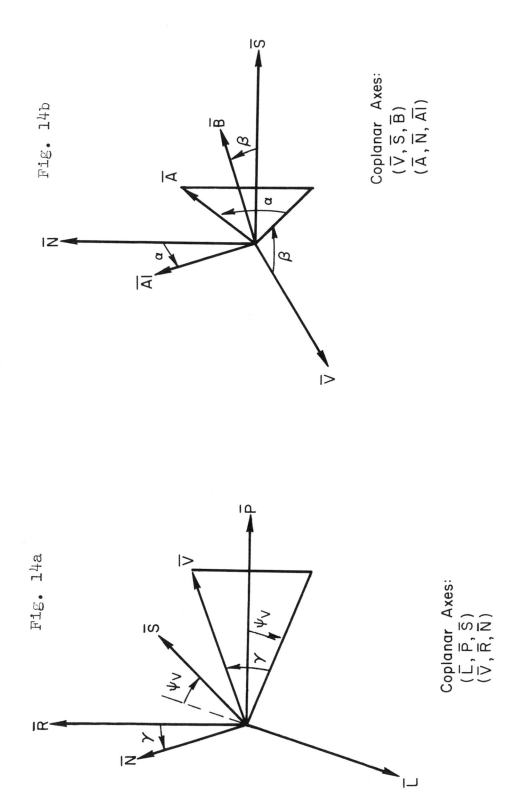

Fig. 14b

Coplanar Axes:
($\bar{V}$, $\bar{S}$, $\bar{B}$)
($\bar{A}$, $\bar{N}$, $\bar{Al}$)

Fig. 14a

Coplanar Axes:
($\bar{L}$, $\bar{P}$, $\bar{S}$)
($\bar{V}$, $\bar{R}$, $\bar{N}$)

Fig. 14- Local-to-Vehicle Coordinate Rotations

$$\begin{pmatrix} F_R \\ F_L \\ F_P \end{pmatrix} = M_2(\Psi_V, \gamma) \begin{pmatrix} F_V \\ F_S \\ F_N \end{pmatrix}$$

where

$$M_2(\Psi_V, \gamma) = \begin{pmatrix} \sin\gamma & 0 & \cos\gamma \\ \cos\gamma\sin\Psi_V & -\cos\Psi_V & -\sin\gamma\sin\Psi_V \\ \cos\gamma\cos\Psi_V & \sin\Psi_V & -\sin\gamma\cos\Psi_V \end{pmatrix} \quad ; \quad (3\text{-}8)$$

$$\begin{pmatrix} F_V \\ F_S \\ F_N \end{pmatrix} = M_1(\beta, \alpha) \begin{pmatrix} F_A \\ F_B \\ F_{Al} \end{pmatrix}$$

where

$$M_1(\beta, \alpha) = \begin{pmatrix} \cos\alpha\cos\beta & -\sin\beta & -\sin\alpha\cos\beta \\ \cos\alpha\sin\beta & \cos\beta & -\sin\alpha\sin\beta \\ \sin\alpha & 0 & \cos\alpha \end{pmatrix} \quad . \quad (3\text{-}9)$$

ROCKET performs the transformations between (F_A, F_B, F_{Al}) and (F_R, F_L, F_P) in two ways, depending on whether the angle β is zero. If $\beta \neq 0$, it uses

$$\begin{pmatrix} F_R \\ F_L \\ F_P \end{pmatrix} = M_2(\Psi v, \ \gamma) \cdot M_1(\beta, \alpha) \cdot \begin{pmatrix} F_A \\ F_B \\ F_{A1} \end{pmatrix}. \qquad (3\text{-}10)$$

If $\beta = 0$, it uses

$$\begin{pmatrix} F_R \\ F_L \\ F_P \end{pmatrix} = M_2(\Psi v, \Theta) \begin{pmatrix} F_A \\ F_B \\ F_{A1} \end{pmatrix} \qquad (3\text{-}11)$$

where $M_2(\Psi v, \Theta)$ is of the same form as $M_2(\Psi v, \gamma)$, except that the vehicle attitude angle $\Theta = \gamma + \alpha$, defined as the angle between the vehicle axis and the local horizontal, replaces the angle γ.

The earth-referenced velocity v_E, and the angles γ and Ψ_v are determined by the following relationships:

$$V_R = \dot{r}$$

$$V_L = r \, \dot{\lambda} \, \cos \phi$$

$$V_P = r \, \dot{\phi}$$

$$v_E = \sqrt{v_R^2 + v_L^2 + v_P^2} \qquad (3\text{-}12)$$

$$\sin \gamma = V_R / v_E$$

$$\tan \Psi_v = V_L / V_P.$$

C. FLIGHT PROGRAM PROCEDURES

As noted before, the flight program is the means by which the user tells ROCKET what nongravitational forces are acting on the vehicle and how the vehicle is oriented with respect to the velocity vector. ROCKET needs this information so that it may correctly resolve the forces into the (R,L,P) system, add the gravitational forces, and then compute and integrate the resulting accelerations.

The flight program for the nth section of a trajectory is a FORTRAN subroutine with the name SECTn. It can be a very complicated subroutine if desired, but in general it consists of a sequence of CALL statements, entered on the Flight Programming Form depicted in Fig. 2 (p. 13), to computational subroutines in the ROCKET library. These subroutines will compute the necessary forces and orientation angles and store them in the places the main program expects them to be. The appropriate places are twelve cells whose program symbols and physical interpretations are given in Table III.

These quantities are the only ones which the user's flight program has to specify how to obtain; ROCKET will take care of the rest of the computations automatically. Furthermore, even these quantities need be specified explicitly by the flight program only when they differ from zero; if any one of these quantities is zero or is not used during a particular section, nothing need be said about it

Table III

QUANTITIES SUPPLIED BY THE USER'S FLIGHT PROGRAM

Program Symbol	Quantity
TAX	thrust T_A along A-axis (lb)
TBT	thrust T_B along B-axis (lb)
TAL	thrust T_{A1} along A1-axis (lb)
AAX	aerodynamic force A_A along A-axis (lb)
ABT	aerodynamic force A_B along B-axis (lb)
AAL	aerodynamic force A_{A1} along A1-axis (lb)
XAX	other nongravitational forces along A-axis (lb)
XBT	other nongravitational forces along B-axis (lb)
XAL	other nongravitational forces along A1-axis (lb)
ALPHAR	angle of attack α (rad)
BETAR	sideslip angle β (rad)
WD	weight derivative or negative fuel flow $\dot{w}$ (lb/sec)

on the Flight Programming Form. The calculating effort is
thus separated into a set of computations which are common
to nearly all trajectory problems and which ROCKET performs
automatically, and another set of computations which are
performed only when desired by the particular user. It is
this separation which accounts for much of the program's
efficiency and flexibility.

The computational subroutines in the ROCKET library
are geared to this scheme. They accept as inputs the
time and the vehicle's position and velocity, or quantities
obtained from these by other computational subroutines,
and produce in various ways either some of the force components and orientation angles of Table III or some
quantities which other subroutines may require to compute
quantities in Table III.

A catalogue of the computational subroutines in the
ROCKET library is given in Appendix B. Propulsion subroutines, described in Appendix B, Sec. 1, furnish the
quantities TAX, TBT, TAL, and WD; aerodynamic subroutines,
described in Sec. 2, furnish AAX, ABT, and AAL; guidance
subroutines, described in Sec. 3, furnish ALPHAR and BETAR.
At present, there are no routines to calculate XAX, XBT,
and XAL, which were added for possible future applications,
but since a quantity which is not specified explicitly
remains equal to zero throughout a section, they do not
cause any trouble.

There is an infinite number of ways to arrive at the above mentioned twelve quantities, given the time, position, and velocity. Needless to say, the ROCKET library does not contain all of them; however, it is quite easy to add a new method to the library, once it has been programmed, and if the method is reasonably straightforward, it will be easy to program. Thus, the capabilities of the program grow with the passage of time and with the addition of useful computational subroutines.

As was remarked above, a great deal of ROCKET's flexibility and efficiency derives from the modular nature of its computational subroutines. Instead of a single large flight program which calculates all possible quantities, usually including a great many undesired ones, a ROCKET flight program consists of a number of small subroutines, each performing a small part of the computation; subroutines furnishing unnecessary quantities are simply not called upon. The price of this flexibility is that the user must be quite careful that each subroutine has been furnished with the prerequisite quantities it needs to carry out its calculation. For example, if a subroutine which calculates an aerodynamic coefficient as a function of Mach number is to be used, the Mach number as a function of the vehicle's position and velocity must be first obtained.

Table IV gives a list of the quantities which are automatically furnished by the ROCKET program as inputs to flight program subroutines. Each subroutine in the catalogues of Appendix B has a category called "Inputs" which enumerates the quantities needed by the subroutine which are <u>not</u> furnished by the program. If a user wishes to use a subroutine requiring such input quantities, he must precede it by one or more subroutines which furnish those quantities. The quantities furnished by a subroutine are enumerated in its "Outputs" category in the catalogue.

A similar situation holds with respect to the termination quantities given in Table II (p. 27). If the user wishes to terminate a section by a quantity not directly furnished by the program (i.e., not in Table IV), he must include in his flight program for the section a subroutine which furnishes that quantity as an output. For example, if one wishes to terminate a section upon reaching a certain inertial velocity v_I, a quantity not directly furnished by ROCKET, a CALL EXTRAP must be included in the flight program for the section, since the subroutine EXTRAP (Appendix B, Sec. 5) furnishes the inertial velocity as an output.

D. A SAMPLE FLIGHT PROGRAM

Suppose that during the second section of a trajectory there is an engine whose performance in terms of thrust and fuel flow has been tabulated as a function of altitude; that the aerodynamic properties of the vehicle have been

Table IV

QUANTITIES AUTOMATICALLY FURNISHED
TO FLIGHT PROGRAM SUBROUTINES

Program Symbol	Quantity
TIME	time t (sec)
ALT,HEFT	altitude h_E above sea level (ft)
ELØNR	longitude λ (rad)
PHIR	latitude ϕ (rad)
VELE,VE	velocity v_E with respect to the earth (ft/sec)
GAMMAR	flight path angle γ (rad)
GAMMAD	flight path angle γ (deg)
SGAM,CGAM	sin γ, cos γ
PSIVR	velocity azimuth angle Ψ_V (rad)
PSIVD	velocity azimuth angle Ψ_V (deg)
SPSIV,CPSIV	sin Ψ_V, cos Ψ_V
RFT	distance r of vehicle from center of earth (ft)
HD	rate of change $\dot{r}$ of radial distance r (ft/sec)
ELD	rate of change $\dot{\lambda}$ of longitude (rad/sec)
PHD	rate of change $\dot{\phi}$ of latitude (rad/sec)
WGT	weight w of vehicle (lbs)

described in terms of axial and normal force coefficients
as tabular functions of Mach number; and that the vehicle
is to be held at a constant angle of attack of one degree.
The flight program would look like this:

```
SUBRØUTINE SECT2
CALL TBTFHE (2)
CALL TABDPQ
CALL MVSDP
CALL TBCAXM (2)
CALL TBCALM (2)
CALL CØNALB (1.,0.)
RETURN
END
```

Comments:

SECT2: The flight program for Section n has
a name of the form SECTn, with $1 \le n \le 20$.

TBTFHE(2) is a propulsion subroutine described
in Appendix B, Sec. 1, and contained in the ROCKET
library. It conducts a table interpolation of order
2 with respect to altitude h_E (an "available"
quantity) to find the thrust, which it places in
location TAX, and the fuel flow, which it places
in location WD after changing its sign. Since no
provision is made for finding TBT and TAL, they are
assumed to be zero.

TABDPQ looks up values of atmospheric density and pressure from tables as functions of altitude, and calculates the dynamic pressure q from the velocity v_E (also an "available" quantity) and density, for use in later calculations. TABDPQ and the following three subroutines are aerodynamic subroutines described in detail in Appendix B, Sec. 2.

MVSDP calculates the speed of sound as a function of the local air density and pressure, and obtains the Mach number as the ratio of vehicle velocity and speed of sound. Note that MVSDP <u>must</u> be preceded by some subroutine which calculates the air density and pressure. If it were not, MVSDP would calculate the speed of sound using for the values of air density and pressure, either zeros or values calculated at some previous time, producing fraudulent results.

TBCAXM(2) conducts a table interpolation of order 2 with respect to Mach number to find the axial force coefficient C_A, and then computes the axial aerodynamic force $A_A = q \cdot A_{ref} \cdot C_A$, which it places in location AAX. Note that to use this routine it is necessary to have on hand the Mach number and the dynamic pressure q. A_{ref}, the reference area of the vehicle, is specified via the Flight Control Form.

TBCALM(2) interpolates in a manner similar to TBCAXM to find $A_{A1} = q \cdot A_{ref} \cdot C_{A1}$, and stores it in location AAL. Another prerequisite for the use of table interpolation subroutines is the presence of the proper table in the proper place; Sec. E below explains how this is accomplished.

CØNALB(1.,0.), a guidance subroutine described in Appendix B, Sec. 3, assumes that the numbers in parentheses are α and β, respectively, expressed in degrees. It converts them to radians and places them in the locations ALPHAR and BETAR. We note that since ABT, XAX, XBT, and XAL are not specified explicitly, they are automatically assumed to be zero.

E. TABLES

By means of tables the user is able to approximate very complicated or even discontinuous mathematical functions whose use may be necessary to describe the environment of a rocket in flight. A user who has such a function of one or two variables (such as the rocket's thrust as a function of altitude, or the vehicle's normal aerodynamic force coefficient as a function of Mach number and angle of attack) need only tabulate the function once on special input forms; it can then be keypunched and entered into a permanent card file of ROCKET tables for subsequent use. Here again the versatility of the program is proportional to the amount of use it gets.

Figures 3 and 4 (pp. 15, 16) show the standard input forms for one- and two-dimensional tables. The number format for the tables is an eight-digit floating point representation; it is a standard one for all ROCKET inputs and is described in Appendix E.

The "table number," the first entry on the input form, provides the program with the information it needs to set up the tables properly. This table number must be the same number as the one which the computational subroutine employing the table assumes is being used. For example, if the flight program uses the subroutine TBTFHE, which assumes that tables of thrust and fuel flow vs. altitude are present in table number 2, and the number 3 is placed in the "table number" slot on the table input form when making up the thrust tables, ROCKET will discontinue the run the first time it calls on the subroutine TBTFHE, and will print the message: "...RUN TERMINATED -- NO THRUST TABLE."

More than one tabular function may be used by a single computational subroutine during the course of a trajectory. This sort of situation is handled by means of the next entry on the input form, the "stage number." As is explained in Appendix C, table number 2 has four stages; i.e., four different tables which can act as table number 2. Thus, when dealing with the two different thrust curves, one may be assigned a stage number of 1, and the other a stage number of 2; thus, both are loaded into different parts of table number 2. During the course of the trajectory, then, the table to be used throughout a section may be specified by placing a 1 or 2 in the "thrust tables" slot in the Section Conditions for that particular section on the Flight Control Form (entry --30, explained in Appendix A, Sec. 2) The nominal value for the stage number is 1; if the slot is left blank, the value 1 will be used. An example of the use of stage numbers is given in Chap. 4, Sec. C.

The "number of entries" refers to the number of entries of the independent variable in the table. On the two-dimensional table input form there are places for the number of entries in both independent variables. These numbers must be less than or equal to the maximum number of entries for the table as given by the "table table," Table V in Appendix C.

The next line on the input form is used only if a blank or zero is in the "table number" position. It is then used to create a table to the user's specification; details are given in Appendix C.

The next line on the form is reserved for a line of comments and identifying remarks about the table; this line will be on the first page of the printed output from the program. The succeeding lines on the form are for the actual numbers comprising the table.

Each dependent variable subtable in the two-dimensional table assumes that the value of the second independent variable is the corresponding value in the second independent variable table. For example, in Fig. 4 the numbers in the "Dependent Variable 3" subtable represent a curve of C_N (the dependent variable) vs. Mach number (the first independent variable) for $\alpha_T = 2$ degrees (the third value of the second independent variable α_T).

In all tables the values of the independent variables must be entered in ascending order.

Chapter 4

EXAMPLES

Four hypothetical trajectory problems are taken as examples, showing how the ROCKET program would be used in their solution. First, the examples show how one might determine the nature of the trajectories which the program could produce in order to contribute toward solution to the problems; second, they show how the necessary ROCKET input forms would be filled out to get the program to calculate these trajectories.

The four examples selected cover many of the fields in which ROCKET trajectories can be helpful, and also employ a number of the special features included in the program, giving the prospective user a better feel for how these features may be exploited.

Setting up these examples is like setting up most actual trajectory problems, in that one depends heavily on the information on the various flight control parameters given in Appendix A, and information on the available flight programs given in Appendix B. To get a full idea of the setting-up process, these appendices should be consulted concurrently with the explanations of the various input entries in the examples. In a sense, one function of the examples is simply to clarify and provide operational definitions for the procedural rules regarding inputs stated in Appendices A and B.

A. EXAMPLE 1: SPUTSPUT I FLIGHT TEST

John Jones has been experimenting with solid pro-
pellant rocketry and has come up with a new fuel and a new
thrust control system which look interesting enough to
flight test. A test rocket, the Sputsput I, now stands
on its launch platform at the firing range, undergoing
some on-site modifications before launch, which is still
a few days away. As Jones wishes the rocket to be re-
covered, but isn't certain what its precise performance
characteristics will be during the flight, he decides to
make a few simulated runs on the ROCKET program to get
an idea of where it will probably land. He also wants to
determine its probable course with respect to a nearby
tracking station associated with the firing range.

The flight will be a simple one-stage affair, with
thrust applied constantly until burnout, after which the
rocket will follow a ballistic trajectory to impact. The
charge geometry assures an essentially constant thrust
level and fuel flow rate, but Jones isn't too sure of the
exact value of the specific impulse of his fuel. In
laboratory tests, it has been averaging about 350 sec,
but he wants to vary this figure by $\pm5\%$ to see how the
trajectory would be affected. The effect of the thrust
control system during the test will be to vary the angle
τ_α between the vehicle axis and the thrust direction by
a succession of linear functions of time. A table

ROCKET ONE-DIMENSIONAL TABLE

2995	t 1	TABLE NO. t o 2	STAGE	t 5 NO. ENTRIES	t o 1			USE ONLY IF TABLE NO. = 0		
0000		BASE LOC.	NO. DER. VAR.	CYCLE						

0000	COMMENTS: SPUTSPUT I LINEAR CONTROL SCHEME - - THRUST ANGLES VS TIME

INDEPENDENT VARIABLE

0000	t 9 t o o	t 5 t o 1	t 1 t o 2	t 2 t 9 2	t 1 t o 3
0005					
0010					
0015					
0020					
0025					
0030					
0035					
0040					
0045					
0050					
0055					
0060					
0065					
0070					

FIRST DEPENDENT VARIABLE

0000	-1 -9	-1 -9	-5 t 9	-5 t o o	t 9 t 9 o
0005					
0010					
0015					
0020					
0025					
0030					
0035					
0040					
0045					
0050					
0055					
0060					
0065					
0070					

SECOND DEPENDENT VARIABLE

0000	t 9 t 9 o	t 9 t o o	t 9 t o o	t 9 t o o	t 9 t 9 o
0005					
0010					
0015					
0020					
0025					
0030					
0035					
0040					
0045					
0050					
0055					
0060					
0065					
0070					

Fig. 15- Thrust Angles vs. Time: Sputsput I

describing this variation has been prepared and appears here as Fig. 15.

The run for the ROCKET program consists of two sections, the first with aerodynamic force and variably-directed thrust forces, and the second with aerodynamic force alone. The set of flight programs and the Flight Control Form for this run are shown in Figs. 16 and 17. Some explanatory remarks on each are given below.

Flight Programs[*]

SECT1

TABDPQ, an aerodynamic subroutine described in Appendix B, Sec. 2, obtains the atmospheric density and pressure from the current altitude of the vehicle by a parabolic interpolation from a table which has been obtained and placed in table number 1. It then computes the dynamic pressure q from the vehicle's current velocity and the atmospheric density.

CϕNCAX(.4), an aerodynamic subroutine, assumes that the vehicle has a constant axial force coefficient C_A of 0.4. The axial aerodynamic force on the vehicle is computed as $A_A = 0.4 \cdot A_{ref} \cdot q$, where A_{ref} is the vehicle's frontal area, which has been placed in the

_____

[*]Subroutine write-ups are found in Appendix B.

```
      SUBRØUTINE SECT1

      CALL TABDPQ
      CALL CØNCAX(.4)
      CALL CTHAIR(2800.,8.,.1)

      CALL TBTATM(10,1)
      CALL
      CALL

      RETURN
      END

      SUBRØUTINE SECT2

      CALL TABDPQ
      CALL CØNCAX(.4)
      CALL

      CALL
      CALL
      CALL

      RETURN
      END

      SUBRØUTINE SECT3

      CALL
      CALL
      CALL

      CALL
      CALL
      CALL

      RETURN
      END
```

```
      SUBRØUTINE SECT4

      CALL
      CALL
      CALL

      CALL
      CALL
      CALL

      RETURN
      END
```

Fig. 16- Flight Programming Form: Sputsput I

appropriate entry of the Flight Control Form
(location 0107 for Section 1), and q is the
dynamic pressure computed in TABDPQ.

CTHAIR(2800.,8.,.1), a propulsion subroutine, assumes an engine with a constant
vacuum thrust T_∞ of 2800 lb, a constant fuel
flow of 8 lb/sec, and an exit area of 0.1 ft^2.
The resultant thrust is computed as T = 2800.
C_T - 0.1 P_A, where P_A is the atmospheric pressure
obtained in TABDPQ, and C_T is the thrust coefficient entered via the Flight Control Form.

TBTATM(10,1), a propulsion subroutine,
assumes that a table of thrust angles τ_α and
τ_β, as functions of time, is located in table
number 10. This has been ensured by setting
the table number equal to 10 on the table input form (Fig. 15). It then conducts a linear
(degree N=1) interpolation to determine τ_α and
τ_β from the current time, and uses Eqs. (B-30)
(Appendix B) to resolve the total thrust T
computed in CTHAIR into its components. Since
in this example τ_β is always zero in this table
(Fig. 15), T_A = T cos τ_α; T_{A1} = T sin τ_α; T_B = 0.

Since no provision is made to calculate
the quantities α, β, A_B, A_{A1}, X_A, X_B, and
X_{A1} in this flight program, they will be assumed

equal to zero throughout the section. In particular, this specifies the vehicle to always be aligned along the velocity vector.

SECT2

The subroutines TABDPQ and CØNCAX(.4) act in the same manner as they did during Section 1. Since no thrust forces are specified during this section, the quantities T_A, T_B, and T_{A1} are assumed to be zero in Section 1.

Flight Control Form[*]

0001. The number 101 will be printed at the left of each line of basic output (see Fig. 30, p. 110). The fourth-order integration method will be used (plus sign).

0002. The spherical earth model has been specified.

0003. The nonrotating earth model has been specified.

0004. Initial latitude is geodetic; initial velocity is earth-referenced.

0005. Initial time = 0.

0006. Initial altitude = 1426 ft.

0007, 0008. Initial latitude and longitude.

0010. For convenience, the initial flight path angle is set to 90° when the initial velocity (0009) is zero, assuring a vertical takeoff.

---

[*]Entries are described in Appendix A.

ROCKET TRAJECTORY PROGRAM—INPUT FORM

DESCRIPTIVE REMARKS

2460	SPUTSPUT I FLIGHT TEST
2470	
2480	J. JONES JAN. 2, 1963
2490	
0000 Ⓐ	

INITIAL CONDITIONS

	SEQUENCE NO.	OBLAT.	ROTAT.	INCON.	
0001	+10 1 +03				
	TIME	ALT.	LAT.	LONG.	VEL.
0005		+1426 +04	+34562 +02	-116248 +03	
	GAMMA	AZIM.	WGT.	LAUNCH LAT.	LAUNCH LONG.
0010		+9 +02	+724 +03		
	INER. REF. LONG.	ALPHA	BETA	N BODY	
0015					
	NO. TRACKERS	LAT. T1	LONG. T1	ALT. T1	LAT. T2
0020	+1 +01	+341136 +02	-116675 +03	+1738 +04	
	LONG. T2	ALT. T2	LAT. T3	LONG. T3	ALT. T3
0025					

SECTION CONDITIONS

	TERMINATION COND.	TERM V1	TERM V2	TERM V3	TERM V4
0100	+2 +01	+395 +03			
0200	-3 +01	+0 +00			
0300					
0400					
	JETT. WGT.	TILT ANGLE	REF. AREA	THRUST COEF.	F.F. COEF.
0105			+1 +01		
0205			+1 +01		
0305					
0405					
	AERO. COEF.	GUID. COEF.	EX. COEF.		
0110					
0210					
0310					
0410					
	MULT. VAL. FLAG.	V1	V2	V3	V4
0115	+8 +01	+95 +00	+1 +01	+105 +01	
0215					
0315					
0415					
	PRINT INTERVAL	AERO. P.Q.	TRACKER P.Q.	ORBIT P.Q.	GUID. P.Q.
0120	+4 +01		+1 +01		
0220	+16 +02		+1 +01		
0320					
0420					
	SPEC. P.O.1	SPEC. P.O. 2	SPEC. P.O. 3	ALT. T.C.	ALT. T.V.
0125					
0225					
0325					
0425					
	THR. TABLES	AERO. TABLES	GUID. TABLES	EX. TABLES	
0130					
0230					
0330					
0430					

EXTRA INPUTS

0000 Ⓐ				Ⓐ : ALWAYS KEYPUNCH THIS CARD	

Fig. 17- Flight Control Form: Sputsput I

0011. Flight is directed due east.

0012. Initial weight of vehicle = 724 lb.

0013. Use 0007, 0008 as launch latitude and longitude.

0020. One tracking station is being specified.

0021. Latitude of tracking station = $34^{\circ}.1136$ N.

0022. Longitude of tracking station = $116^{\circ}.1675$ W.

0023. Altitude of tracking station = 1738 ft.

0100. Terminate Section 1 by weight (termination quantity number 2; see Table II, p. 27).

0101. Terminate Section 1 when w = 395 lb (burnout weight).

0107. Frontal area A_{ref} of vehicle = 1 ft^2 during Section 1.

0115. Multiple values are requested for section quantity 8, the thrust coefficient C_T (p. 132).

0116-
0118. Section 1 will be run three times, the first time with the value of the vacuum thrust T_{∞} multiplied by 0.95, the second time by 1.0, and the third time by 1.05. Each of these three branches will be propagated through Section 2, giving three trajectories resulting from 5% low, nominal, and 5% high values of the rocket's specific impulse (the fuel flow rate is not varied from branch to branch).

0120. Print every four seconds during Section 1.

0123. Print range, azimuth, and elevation with respect to tracking station specified in 0021-0023 every four seconds during Section 1.

0200. Terminate Section 2 by altitude h_E (termination quantity 3). Use parabolic interpolation to find endpoint (minus sign).

0201. Terminate Section 2 when $h_E = 0$ (this slot could have been left blank, with the same result).

0207. Reference area $A_{ref} = 1$ ft^2 during Section 2.

0220. Print every 16 seconds during Section 2.

0223. Print tracking quantities every 16 seconds during Section 2.

0300. A blank or zero here means no further sections remain to be processed.

After the inputs have been keypunched from the forms onto cards,[*] the run deck has been set up in the proper fashion (see Chap. 2, Sec. A), and the job run on the computer, a printout of the compiled flight programs, the numerical inputs, and the basic output quantities and tracking functions along the trajectory for each of the three specified branches will be produced. The printout of the numerical inputs and first page of trajectory output appear as Figs. 29 and 30 (pp. 109, 110). The information of particular interest is shown below.

Vacuum I_{SP} (sec)	Impact Latitude (deg)	Impact Longitude (deg)	Range (n mi)	Flight Time (sec)	Apogee Altitude (ft)	Impact Velocity (ft/sec)
332.5	34.155	-115.684	28.032	285.0	255,900	1637
350.0	34.155	-115.621	31.177	305.0	297,200	1727
367.5	34.154	-115.553	34.568	324.4	341,700	1819

---

[*]Lines on Flight Control Forms or table input forms with no written entries should not be keypunched; nor should unused flight program subroutines or CALL statements on the Flight Programming Form be keypunched.

B. EXAMPLE 2: THE SPACE TAXI

A space station is heading eastward in an equatorial orbit, and Q. Smith is interested in returning a space taxi from it to a given point on earth. This space taxi has available a retro-rocket which can place it at an altitude of 400,000 ft with a velocity of 20,000 ft/sec and a flight path angle of -1^O, at a distance of 30° along the orbit from the point of retro-firing. At this point a lifting re-entry into the atmosphere is initiated, with a drag force specified by the table of axial force coefficient vs. Mach number in Fig. 18, and a constant normal-to-axial aerodynamic force ratio $A_{A1}/A_A = 2$. A constant bank angle σ_B is maintained throughout the flight; thus, a component of the normal aerodynamic force is available to divert the vehicle away from the equatorial plane. What choice of σ_B and λ_F, the longitude of retro-firing, will produce a landing at the Caracas spaceport, at latitude $\phi_L = 10^O$ N and longitude $\lambda_L = 67^O$ W?

Here is one method of solving this problem with the aid of the ROCKET program, and at the same time providing the solution of the general problem of choosing the bank angle σ_B and retro-firing longitude λ_F necessary to land at any latitude ϕ_L and longitude λ_L which can be reached by the vehicle.

Assume an initial retro-firing longitude $\lambda_F = 0$; then the initial conditions at the altitude of 400,000 ft are

ROCKET ONE-DIMENSIONAL TABLE

1 4	6	15 17 19	28 30 32	41 43 45	54 56 58	67 69
2995	+5 TABLE NO. +01	STAGE	+5 NO. ENTRIES +02		USE ONLY IF TABLE NO. = 0	
0000	BASE LOC.	NO. DEP. VAR.	CYCLE			

0000	COMMENTS AXIAL FORCE COEFF. VS MACH NO. SPACE TAXI

INDEPENDENT VARIABLE

	6	15 17 19	28 30 32	41 43 45	54 56 58	67 69
0000	+0 +00	+4 +00	+6 +00	+8 +00	+9 +00
0005	+1 +01	+11 +01	+125 +01	+15 +01	+2 +01
0010	+3 +01	+4 +01	+6 +01	+1 +02	+5 +02
0015					
0020					
0025					
0030					
0035					
0040					
0045					
0050					
0055					
0060					
0065					
0070					

FIRST DEPENDENT VARIABLE

0000	+5 +00	+52 +00	+55 +00	+6 +00	+8 +00
0005	+11 +01	+105 +01	+8 +00	+4 +00	+5 +00
0010	+45 +00	+4 +00	+4 +00	+4 +00	+4 +00
0015					
0020					
0025					
0030					
0035					
0040					
0045					
0050					
0055					
0060					
0065					
0070					

SECOND DEPENDENT VARIABLE

0000					
0005					
0010					
0015					
0020					
0025					
0030					
0035					
0040					
0045					
0050					
0055					
0060					
0065					
0070					

Fig. 18- Axial Force Coefficient vs. Mach Number: Space Taxi

given at a latitude of $0°$ and a longitude of $30°$ E. Run eight re-entry trajectories on the ROCKET program, using the multiple-branch and multiple-run capabilities of the program, with bank angles varying from $0°$ to $70°$ in increments of $10°$; each trajectory will produce a different latitude and longitude of landing.

The landing latitude ϕ_L can then be plotted as a function of σ_B (see Fig. 19a), and the value of σ_B corresponding to $\phi_L - 10°$ (or any desired latitude ϕ_L which can be reached) obtained by interpolation. The landing longitude λ_{Lo}, relative to a retro-firing longitude of zero, can be considered as the descent range of the vehicle corresponding to a choice of σ_B; it can be plotted as a function of σ_B (Fig. 19b) and the descent range corresponding to the desired σ_B obtained by interpolation. The actual longitude of retro-firing is then given by the longitude of the landing point minus the descent range, $\lambda_F = \lambda_L - \lambda_{Lo}$. In order to land at the Caracas spaceport, then, the flight would be at a bank angle of either $13°.7$ or $65°.5$, producing a descent range of either $90°$ or $49°.5$. Thus, the longitude of retro-firing could be either $157°$ W using the bank angle $\sigma_B = 13°.7$, or $116°.5$ W using $\sigma_B = 63°.5$. Further reference to the printout for the various bank angles would show that the maximum deceleration experienced at a bank angle of $13°.7$ is about 3.5 g, while that at a bank angle of $63°.5$ is about 8.8 g, so the choice $\sigma_B = 13°.7$ might be preferred.

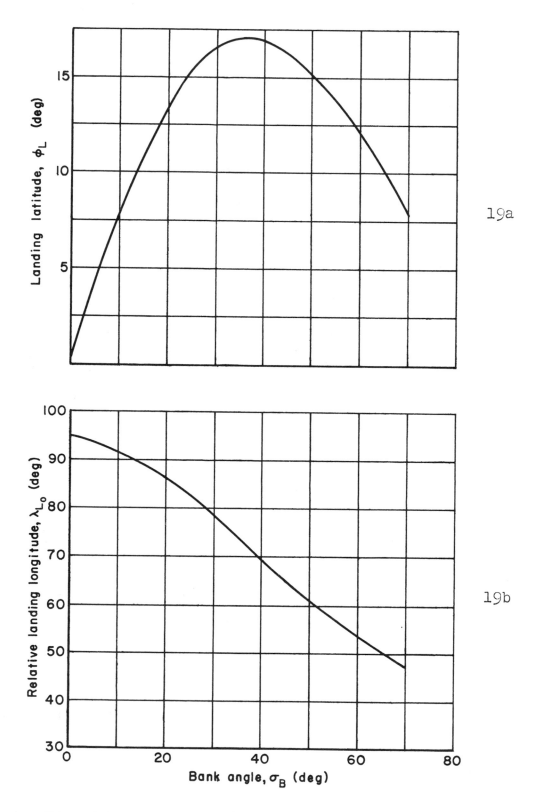

19a

19b

Fig. 19- Space Taxi Descent Relationships

The input forms describing the desired series of trajectories are shown in Figs. 20-22 below. Since there are no points of discontinuity in the vehicle's flight environment throughout the trajectory, only one section is needed, terminating when the altitude reaches zero. No propulsive forces are used during the re-entry, and, for simplicity, guidance is handled by assuming that the vehicle axis is always oriented along the velocity vector (i.e., $\alpha = \beta = 0$); thus, no propulsion or guidance sub routines are needed in the flight program, as unspecified quantities are assumed to be zero throughout the section.

A number of aerodynamic subroutines will be needed to specify the forces acting on the vehicle, however. We look for one which supplies the forces resulting from a constant bank angle among those described in the catalogue given in Appendix B, Sec. 2, and find that the subroutine CBANKA (BA) fills the bill, taking the argument BA multiplied by the section coefficient C_{EXT} as the bank angle and resolving the normal aerodynamic forces AAL and ABT accordingly. However, it needs as an input an original estimate of the normal force acting on the vehicle stored in the location AAL; this is obtained by the subroutine CØNRFA (ALØA) which assumes that the argument ALØA is the ratio A_{A1}/A_A of the normal force to the axial force AAX. The axial force is computed by the subroutine TBCAXM (N), using the table of drag coefficient vs. Mach number

(Fig. 18); the Mach number is obtained by the subroutine MVSDP, which in turn requires the subroutine TABDPQ to provide values of air density and pressure. Since TABDPQ requires no inputs other than those furnished directly by the ROCKET program (and the table of air density and pressure vs. altitude which is placed in table number 1), no further aerodynamic subroutines are required. The resulting flight program is shown in Fig. 20.

A detailed explanation of the quantities entered on the Flight Control Form is given below.

Flight Control Form: First Run

0001. The identifying integer "201" will be printed at the left of each line of basic output. Plus sign specifies fourth-order integration.

0002. Since this entry is blank, the spherical earth model has been specified.

0003. The rotating earth model has been specified.

0004. Initial longitude is geocentric; initial velocity is earth-referenced.

0006. Initial altitude = 400,000 ft.

0008. Initial longitude = 30° E.

0009. Initial velocity = 20,000 ft/sec.

0010. Initial flight path angle = -1°.

0011. Initial velocity azimuth = 90°.

0012. Weight of vehicle = 20,000 lb.

0100. Terminate Section 1 by altitude (termination quantity number 3; see Table II); use parabolic interpolation to find terminal altitude.

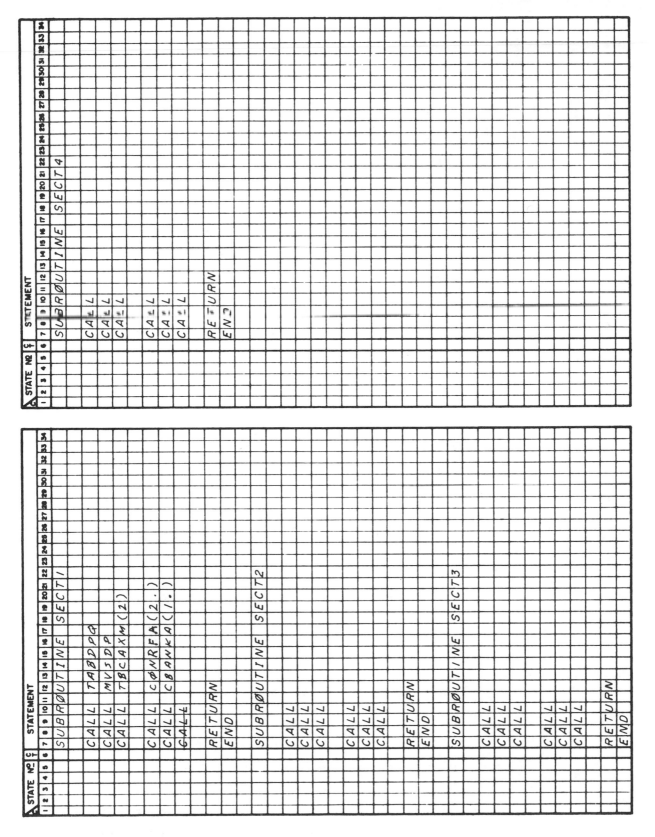

Fig. 20- Flight Programming Form: Space Taxi

0101. Terminal altitude = 0.

0107. Reference area of vehicle A_{ref} = 20 ft^2.

0115. Multiple values are requested for section quantity 12, the coefficient C_{EX} (p. 132).

0116-
0119. Section 1 will be run four times; the first time, the unit bank angle given in the flight program (Fig. 20) will be multiplied by C_{EX} = 70, producing a 70° bank angle trajectory. The succeeding three branch trajectories will run at bank angles of 60°, 50°, and 40°.

0120. Print every eight seconds during Section 1.

0121. Print extra aerodynamic output every eight seconds.

Flight Control Form: Second Run

This input form illustrates the use of ROCKET's multiple-run capability. The cards punched from this form would be placed directly behind those punched from the form in Fig. 21. After ROCKET finishes the trajectories resulting from the input of Fig. 21, it will return and read in the input of Fig. 22 as changes from the original input, and then compute the trajectories resulting from the modified input.

2470. This line of comments will be printed out instead of the line corresponding to 2470 on the input form of Fig. 21.

0001. This set of trajectories will have the identifying integer "202".

0003. As this entry is blank, no change is made from the previous run; the rotating earth model will be used during this set of

ROCKET TRAJECTORY PROGRAM—INPUT FORM

DESCRIPTIVE REMARKS

2460	SPACE TAXI INVESTIGATION
2470	BANK ANGLES, 70, 60, 50, 40 DEG.
2480	Q. SMITH AUG. 12, 1962
2490	
0000	(A)

INITIAL CONDITIONS

	SEQUENCE NO.	OBLAT.	ROTAT.	INCON.	
0001	+20, +03		+1, +01	+2, +01	
0005	TIME / ALT. +4, +06	LAT.	LONG. +3, +02	+2, VEL. +P5	
0010	GAMMA -1, +01	AZIM. +9, +02	WGT. +2, +05	LAUNCH LAT.	LAUNCH LONG.
0015	INER. REF. LONG.	ALPHA	BETA	N BODY	
0020	NO. TRACKERS	LAT. T1	LONG. T1	ALT. T1	LAT. T2
0025	LONG. T2	ALT. T2	LAT. T3	LONG. T3	ALT. T3

SECTION CONDITIONS

	TERMINATION COND.	TERM V1	TERM V2	TERM V3	TERM V4
0100	-3, +01				
0200					
0300					
0400					

	JETT. WGT.	TILT ANGLE	REF. AREA	THRUST COEF	F.F. COEF.
0105			+2, +02		
0205					
0305					
0405					

	AERO. COEF.	GUID. COEF.	EX. COEF.		
0110					
0210					
0310					
0410					

	MULT. VAL. FLAG.	V1	V2	V3	V4
0115	+12, +92	+7, +02	+6, +02	+5, +02	+4, +02
0215					
0315					
0415					

	PRINT INTERVAL	AERO. P.Q.	TRACKER P.Q.	ORBIT P.Q.	GUID. P.Q.
0120	+8, +91	+1, +91			
0220					
0320					
0420					

	SPEC. P.Q.1	SPEC. P.Q.2	SPEC. P.Q.3	ALT. T.C.	ALT. T.V.
0125					
0225					
0325					
0425					

	THR. TABLES	AERO. TABLES	GUID. TABLES	EX. TABLES	
0130					
0230					
0330					
0430					

EXTRA INPUTS

0000 (A)				(A) : ALWAYS KEYPUNCH THIS CARD

Fig. 21- Flight Control Form for First Run:
Space Taxi

ROCKET TRAJECTORY PROGRAM—INPUT FORM

DESCRIPTIVE REMARKS

2460	
2470	BANK ANGLES 30, 20, 10, 0 DEG.
2480	
2490	
0000 (A)	

INITIAL CONDITIONS

0001	SEQUENCE NO. +202 +03	OBLAT.	ROTAT.	INCON.	
0005	TIME	ALT.	LAT.	LONG.	VEL.
0010	GAMMA	AZIM.	WGT.	LAUNCH LAT.	LAUNCH LONG.
0015	INER. REF. LONG.	ALPHA	BETA	N BODY	
0020	NO. TRACKERS	LAT. T1	LONG. T1	ALT. T1	LAT. T2
0025	LONG. T2	ALT. T2	LAT. T3	LONG. T3	ALT. T3

SECTION CONDITIONS

| | TERMINATION COND. | TERM V1 | TERM V2 | TERM V3 | TERM V4 |
| 0100 / 0200 / 0300 / 0400 | | | | | |

| | JETT. WGT. | TILT ANGLE | REF. AREA | THRUST COEF | F.F. COEF. |
| 0105 / 0205 / 0305 / 0405 | | | | | |

| | AERO. COEF. | GUID. COEF. | EX. COEF. | | |
| 0110 / 0210 / 0310 / 0410 | | | | | |

	MULT. VAL. FLAG.	V1	V2	V3	V4
0115		+3 +02	+2 +02	+1 +02	+1 -10
0215 / 0315 / 0415					

| | PRINT INTERVAL | AERO. P.Q. | TRACKER P.Q. | ORBIT P.Q. | GUID. P.Q. |
| 0120 / 0220 / 0320 / 0420 | | | | | |

| | SPEC. P.O.1 | SPEC. P.O.2 | SPEC. P.O.3 | ALT. T.C. | ALT. T.V. |
| 0125 / 0225 / 0325 / 0425 | | | | | |

| | THR. TABLES | AERO. TABLES | GUID. TABLES | EX. TABLES | |
| 0130 / 0230 / 0330 / 0430 | | | | | |

EXTRA INPUTS

| 0000 (A) | | | | (A): ALWAYS KEYPUNCH THIS CARD |

Fig. 22-Flight Control Form for Second Run:
Space Taxi

trajectories. Similarly, the rest of the
initial conditions will be the same as
those of the previous run.

0116-
0118.
The first three trajectories of this run
will employ bank angles of 30°, 20°, and
10°, respectively.

0119.
If a zero were placed in this entry, ROCKET
would assume that no further branch trajectories beyond the third one were desired
during this section (Chap. 2, Sec. D).
Placing an extremely small nonzero quantity
in this entry will cause the program to run
a fourth branch trajectory with a bank angle
effectively equal to zero degrees. This
trick can usually be employed in places where,
for various reasons of convenience, ROCKET
makes special assumptions about zero entries.

C.   EXAMPLE 3:   THE ANTIGUA VENUS PROBE

Joe Miller is investigating possible applications of
the Antigua booster, a hypothetical vehicle in the next
generation beyond the Nova. One of these applications
concerns a design variation on a manned Venus probe, involving, in addition, the use of a possible equatorial
launch site at Jarvis Island. As a first step in the
study, he decides to run a simple set of ascent variations,
involving two Antigua booster engines in the first stage
and two possible advanced Nova boosters as a second stage,
in order to get a feel for the flight regimes traversed
by the vehicle in the ascent phase of the mission.

Tables of thrust and fuel flow vs. altitude for the

ROCKET ONE-DIMENSIONAL TABLE

2995	TABLE NO. +2 +01	STAGE +2 +01	NO. ENTRIES +17 +02		USE ONLY IF TABLE NO. = 0
0000	BASE LOC.	NO. DEP. VAR.	CYCLE		

0000	COMMENTS THRUST, FUEL FLOW VS ALTITUDE -- 2ND STAGE MARK BOOSTERS

INDEPENDENT VARIABLE

0000	+9	+00	+12	+05	+14	+05	+6	+05	+8 +05
0005	+1	+06	+112	+06	+114	+06	+16	+06	+18 +06
0010	+2	+06	+24	+96	+3	+06	+4	+06	+6 +06
0015	+1	+97	+1	+08					

FIRST DEPENDENT VARIABLE

0000	+87	+07	+905	+07	+93	+07	+95	+07	+97 +97
0005	+985	+07	+1	+08	+101	+08	+102	+08	+103 +08
0010	+1035	+08	+104	+08	+1045	+98	+105	+08	+105 +08
0015	+105	+08	+105	+98					

SECOND DEPENDENT VARIABLE

0000	+4	+05	+41	+05	+408	+05	+406	+05	+409 +05
0005	+402	+05	+401	+05	+4	+05	+4	+05	+399 +95
0010	+399	+05	+398	+95	+397	+05	+396	+05	+395 +05
0015	+395	+05	+395	+05					

Fig. 23- Thrust and Fuel Flow: Antigua Venus Probe

Novas and the proposed Antiguas (the former table appears as Fig. 23), are put together, and a table of the axial aerodynamic force coefficient C_A as a function of Mach number for the design configuration is determined.

Joe decides on a three-section ascent for the initial run (see Fig. 24); a vertical liftoff for the first 25 seconds of powered flight, followed by a gravity turn (zero angle of attack) throughout the second section, the remainder of the Antigua stage, after which the booster is jettisoned and the Nova propels the vehicle through a third section characterized by a constant inertial attitude angle, which has been selected for its property of near-maximizing orbital energy. To initiate the gravity turn in the second section, the imprecise but simple expedient of an instantaneous tilt of the vehicle and the velocity vector directly after the liftoff section is to be used; since this can be a somewhat touchy maneuver, a number of different tilt angles will be tried. The basic information desired is a running printout during the third section of the vehicle's osculating orbital elements and orbital energy; once a feel for these quantities has been established, more precise ascent studies will be conducted, and planning of the latter stages of the Venus journey will be initiated.

The set of flight programs and the Flight Control Form for this first run are shown in Figs. 25 and 26, with

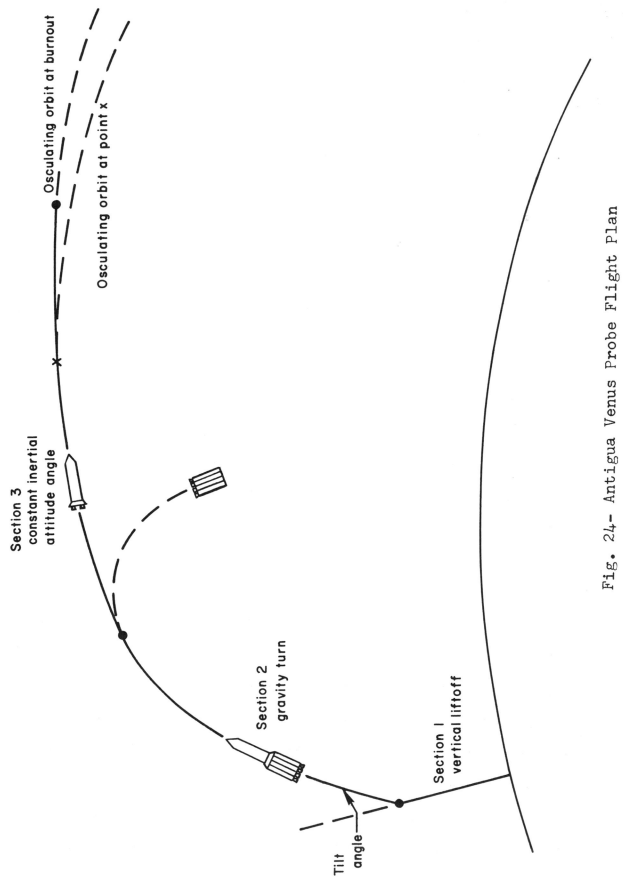

Fig. 24- Antigua Venus Probe Flight Plan

explanatory remarks on each given below.

Flight Programs

SECT1

UPUPUP assures that during Section 1 the
vehicle will be flying vertically.

TABDPQ obtains the atmospheric density and
pressure from a standard table vs. altitude which
has been obtained and placed in table number 1; it
then computes the dynamic pressure q from the
current velocity.

MVSDP computes the local speed of sound from
the atmospheric density and pressure, and uses it
to compute the Mach number.

TBCAXM(2) conducts an interpolation of order
2 to find the axial aerodynamic force coefficient
C_A as a function of Mach number from the table
which has been made up and placed in table number
5. It then takes the dynamic pressure q which was
computed in TABDPQ and the vehicle's reference area
A_{ref} which has been placed in the Flight Control
Form (location 0107) and uses them along with C_A
to compute the axial aerodynamic force by Eq. (B-34).

TBTFHE(2) conducts an interpolation of order
2 to find the axial thrust and the fuel flow as a
function of altitude from the table which has been
set up and placed in table number 2.

```
SUBROUTINE SECT4
       CALL
       CALL
       CALL
       CALL
       CALL
       CALL
       RETURN
       END
```

```
SUBROUTINE SECT1
       CALL  UPUPUP
       CALL  TABDPQ
       CALL  MVSDP
       CALL  TBCAXM(2)
       CALL  TBTFHE(2)
       CALL
       RETURN
       END
SUBROUTINE SECT2
       CALL  CONALB(0.,0.)
       CALL  TABDPQ
       CALL  MVSDP
       CALL  TBCAXM(2)
       CALL  TBTFHE(2)
       CALL
       RETURN
       END
SUBROUTINE SECT3
       CALL  CONTID(0.)
       CALL  TABDPQ
       CALL  MVSDP
       CALL  TBCAXM(2)
       CALL  CONCLAC(.1)
       CALL  TBTFHE(2)
       RETURN
       END
```

Fig. 25- Flight Programming Form: Venus Probe

Generally, guidance subroutines precede aerodynamic subroutines, which in turn precede propulsion subroutines in a flight program, because aerodynamic quantities often depend on things like the angle of attack α, which are found in the guidance routines, and propulsion computations can depend on aerodynamic quantities such as atmospheric pressure.

No provision has been made in this section's flight program for non-axial thrust or aerodynamic forces. In such a case ROCKET assumes they are zero.

Note that the flight program for this section could have been specified by a single reference, CALL UPUP1, to the macro-subroutine UPUP1 (see Appendix B, Sec. 6).

SECT2

CØNALB(0.,0.) sets the angle of attack α and the sideslip angle β to zero during Section 2. Actually, this reference is redundant, since they are assumed to be zero anyway.

The rest of the quantities are calculated in the same manner as Section 1.

The flight program for this section could have been specified by the macro-subroutine reference CALL GTURN1.

SECT3

CØNTID(0.) specifies that the rate of change of the interial attitude angle θ_I be zero; i.e., that θ_I remain constant throughout Section 3. The angle of attack α is then calculated as a dependent variable from Eq. (B-43); the sideslip angle β is assumed to be zero.

CϕNCLA(.1) assumes that the Al-axis aerodynamic force coefficient C_{Al} is proportional to α; in fact, that $C_{Al} = 0.1\ \alpha$. It then uses the dynamic pressure q and the reference area A_{ref} to compute the aerodynamic force A_{Al} along the Al-axis by Eq. (B-33).

The rest of the quantities are calculated in the same manner as in Sections 1 and 2. Note, however that to take account of the dropping of the booster, a different reference area is being used (location 0307 below), and a different table of thrust and fuel flow vs. altitude, which has been placed in the stage 2 portion of table number 2 (see Fig. 23 above), is being referred to (location 0300).

Flight Control Form

0001. The identifying integer "301" will be printed at the left of each line of basic output. Minus sign specifies second-order integration.
0002. The oblate earth model has been specified.
0003. The rotating earth model has been specified.
0004. Launch latitude is geocentric; initial velocity is earth-referenced.
0006. Launch at sea level.
0007, 0008. Hypothetical Jarvis Island launch complex.

ROCKET TRAJECTORY PROGRAM—INPUT FORM

DESCRIPTIVE REMARKS

	1 4 6 10 15 20 25 30 35 40 45 50 55 60 65
2460	VENUS, PROBE - 1 - FIRST CUT
2470	
2480	MILLER OCTOBER 1961
2490	
0000	(A)

INITIAL CONDITIONS

	1 4 6 15 17 19 28 30 32 41 43 45 54 56 58 67 69
0001	SEQUENCE NO. -3Ø1 +Ø3 OBLAT. +1 +Ø1 ROTAT. +1 +Ø1 +2 INCON. +1 +Ø1 /////
0005	TIME ALT. -5 +ØØ LAT. -6 +Ø3 LONG. VEL.
0010	GAMMA +9 AZIM. +2 +Ø2 WGT. +2 +Ø8 LAUNCH LAT. LAUNCH LONG.
0015	INER. REF. LONG. ALPHA BETA N BODY
0020	NO. TRACKERS LAT. T1 LONG. T1 ALT. T1 LAT. T2
0025	LONG. T2 ALT. T2 LAT. T3 LONG. T3 ALT. T3

SECTION CONDITIONS

	TERMINATION COND.	TERM V1	TERM V2	TERM V3	TERM V4
0100	+1 +Ø1 +2,Ø	+Ø3			
0200	+2 +Ø1 +65	+Ø7			
0300	+2 +Ø1 +1	+97			
0400					

	JETT. WGT.	TILT ANGLE	REF. AREA	THRUST COEF	F.F. COEF.
0105			+3 +Ø3		
0205			+3 +Ø3		
0305	+1.5 +Ø7		+1.5 +Ø3		
0405					

	AERO. COEF.	GUID. COEF.	EX. COEF.		
0110					
0210					
0310					
0410					

	MULT. VAL. FLAG.	V1	V2	V3	V4
0115					
0215	+6 +Ø1	+1 +Ø1	+15 +Ø1	+2 +Ø1	+12.5 +Ø1
0315	+8 +Ø1	+8 +ØØ	+1 +Ø1	+12 +Ø1	
0415					

	PRINT INTERVAL	AERO. P.O.	TRACKER P.O.	ORBIT P.O.	GUID. P.O.
0120	+9 +Ø1				
0220	+8 +Ø1	+1 +Ø1			
0320	+8 +Ø1	+1 +Ø1		+1 +Ø1	
0420					

	SPEC. P.O.1	SPEC. P.O.2	SPEC. P.O.3	ALT. T.C.	ALT. T.V.
0125					
0225					
0325				+8 +Ø1	+1 +Ø2
0425					

	THR. TABLES	AERO. TABLES	GUID. TABLES	EX. TABLES	
0130					
0230					
0330	+2 +Ø1				
0430					

EXTRA INPUTS

0000	(A)		(A) : ALWAYS KEYPUNCH THIS CARD		

Fig. 26- Flight Control Form: Venus Probe

0011. Eastward launch.

0012. Initial weight of vehicle = 20,000,000 lb.

0100. Terminate Section 1 by time (termination quantity number 1; see Table II).

0101. Terminate Section 1 when t = 25 sec.

0107. Reference area of vehicle A_{ref} = 300 ft^2 during Section 1.

0120. Print every four seconds during Section 1.

0130, 0131. Thrust and aerodynamic tables assumed to be in stage 1 (p. 135).

0200. Terminate second section by weight (termination quantity number 2).

0201. Terminate second section when w = 6,500,000 lb.

0215. Multiple values are requested for section quantity 6, the tilt angle (p. 131).

0216- 0219. Section 2 will be run four times, with tilt angles of 1, 1.5, 2, and 2.5 degrees (i.e., the velocity vector and vehicle's axis will be instantaneously rotated through 1, 1.5, 2, and 2.5 degrees in the launch azimuth plane at the beginning of the section).

0220. Print every eight seconds during Section 2.

0221. Print extra aerodynamic output every eight seconds.

0300. Terminate third section by weight (termination quantity number 2).

0301. Terminate third section when w = 1,000,000 lb.

0305. Jettison 1,500,000 lb (the booster stage) at the beginning of Section 3.

0307. New reference area A_{ref} = 150 ft^2 during Section 3.

0315. Multiple values are requested for section quantity 8, the thrust coefficient.

0316-
0318. Each of the four branches created in Section 2 by the different tilt angles will be run through Section 3 three times, with the thrust values (obtained from the table) being multiplied throughout by 0.8, 1.0, and 1.2 (representing possible pessimistic, expected, and optimistic estimates of the specific impulse of the upper stage Nova engines).

0320. Print every eight seconds during Section 3.

0321. Print extra aerodynamic output every eight seconds.

0323. Print extra orbital output every eight seconds. The orbital elements printed out at a point are those which would result if all thrust and aerodynamic forces were cut off at that point, assuming a homogeneous spherical earth.

0328. Use axial acceleration (termination quantity number 8) as an alternate termination quantity.

0329. If the axial acceleration reaches 10 g's before the weight gets down to 1,000,000 lb in any of the twelve branches of Section 3, the branch is terminated at that point.

0330. Basic values of thrust and fuel flow during this section are taken from a table vs. altitude located in stage 2 of the propulsion table (number 2); this table (Fig. 23) defines the performance of the engines in the Nova stage.

D. EXAMPLE 4: MARTIAN RENDEZVOUS

Jim Doe wishes to design a vehicle which will take off from the surface of Mars and rendezvous with a vehicle circling Mars at an orbital altitude of 100 n mi. In executing the rendezvous, he wants to employ the simplest possible plan of ascent: a vertical rise until a certain velocity is reached, at which point a pitch-over maneuver is executed, followed by a gravity turn until thrust is cut off at a point where the extrapolated apogee altitude is 100 n mi. The vehicle coasts to apogee, then applies an impulse sufficient to circularize its orbit. He is interested in finding the pitch-over angle which maximizes the ratio of final weight in circular orbit to launch weight, and the corresponding thrust cutoff conditions.

This sort of problem can be solved to any desired degree of accuracy by means of the simple maximization scheme described in Chap. 2, Sec. E, utilizing the orbit circularization option available with the orbital output (Chap. 5, Sec. E). Doe plans a very short initial vertical takeoff, executing the instantaneous pitch-over maneuver at the point at which the vehicle has reached a velocity of 25 ft/sec. At this point he is reasonably sure that the maximum weight ratio will be attained with a tilt angle θ_T somewhere between $0^\circ.1$ and 5°, and that the weight ratio will be a smooth concave function of tilt angle within this region. The iteration is then set up by composing an ITER8 subroutine consisting of a reference to the maximization subroutine FIBITR, and supplying it with the lower and upper bounds of the tilt angle interval via the Flight Control Form.

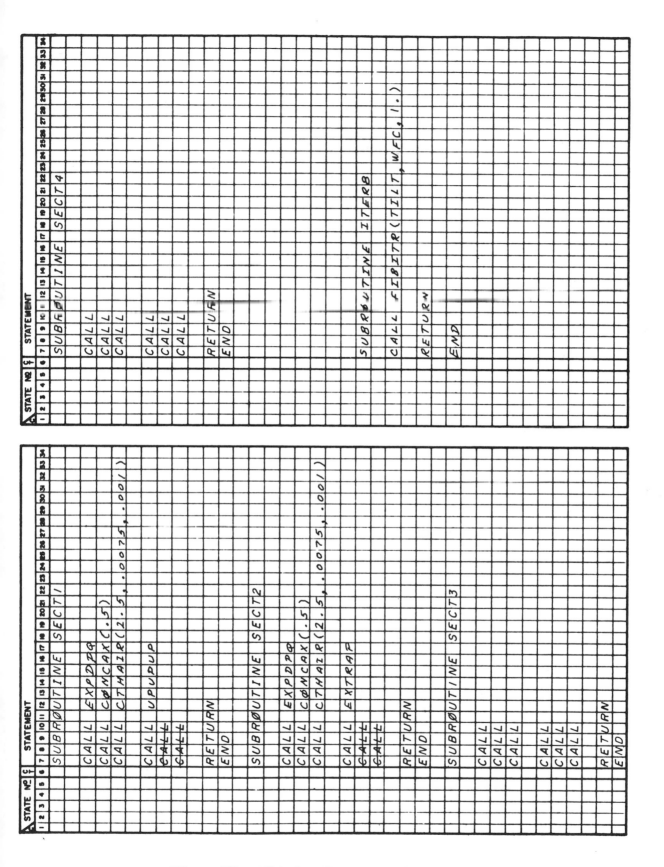

Fig. 27- Flight Programming Form:
Martian Rendezvous

For the sake of generality, Doe decides to run the trajectories with respect to a unit takeoff weight. This can be done quite simply by placing a 1. in the initial weight slot and using ratios to specify thrust, reference area, and the like. Also, a number of necessary Martian physical parameters are obtained,[2] and entered into the program via the Extra Inputs entries on the Flight Control Form. The Flight Programming Form for this problem is shown in Fig. 27, and the Flight Control Form in Fig. 28. Descriptive remarks on each are given below.

Flight Programs

SECT1

EXPDPQ obtains atmospheric density and pressure as a function of altitude by means of an exponential model atmosphere. The density ρ_A is computed as $\rho_A = \rho_{SL} e^{-\beta_A h_E}$ and the pressure P_A as $P_A = g_o \rho_A / \beta_A$, where the sea-level density ρ_{SL}, the decay factor β_A (the reciprocal of the scale height), and the mass conversion factor g_o are adjustable program constants. As the nominal values of these constants are earth-referenced, their Martian counterparts are entered into the program via the Extra Inputs portion of the Flight Control Form for use during this run. This subroutine also computes the dynamic pressure q from the density and the vehicle's velocity.

CØNCAX(.5) assumes that the vehicle has a constant axial force coefficient C_A of 0.5. The axial aerodynamic force on the vehicle is computed as $A_A = 0.5 \cdot A_{ref} \cdot q$, where A_{ref} is the vehicle's frontal area, which has been placed in location 0107 of the Flight Control Form, and q is the dynamic pressure computed in EXPDPQ.

CTHAIR(2.5, .0075, .001) assumes a rocket engine with a constant vacuum thrust of T_w of 2.5 lb, a constant fuel flow of .0075 lb, and an exit area of .001 ft^2. As the trajectories are to be run with respect to a unit takeoff weight (w_o = 1 lb on the Flight Control Form, location 0012), these quantities actually represent vacuum-thrust-to-initial-weight ratio, and exit-area-to-initial-weight ratio. The resultant thrust-to-initial-weight ratio is computed as $T = 2.5 - .001 P_A$, where P_A is the atmospheric pressure obtained in EXPDPQ.

UPUPUP assures that during Section 1 the vehicle will be flying vertically.

SECT2

The subroutines EXPDPQ, CØNCAX(.5), and CTHAIR (2.5, .0075, .001) act in the same manner as they did in Section 1. Since no guidance subroutines are specified, the angle of attack α and sideslip angle β are assumed to be zero, effecting a gravity turn during this section.

EXTRAP is a miscellaneous computational sub-routine described in Appendix B, Sec. 5. It computes a number of parameters related to the osculating orbit resulting from a vacuum ballistic extrapolation of the vehicle's current position and velocity, including the extrapolated apogee altitude h_A. It is this quantity which is being used to terminate the section, so provision must be made to calculate it at each step.

ITER8

The subroutine FIBITR (TILT, WFC, 1.) iterates Section 2 eight times to find the approximate tilt angle Θ_T which maximizes the final weight w_{FC} in a 100-n mi circular orbit. TILT and WFC are the program symbols for Θ_T and w_{FC}, obtained from the List of Symbols, and the 1. indicates a maximum rather than a minimum is being sought. Since ITER8 contains references to ROCKET program symbols, it must be compiled with a COMMON package (see Appendix E, Sec. 5).

Flight Control Form

0001. The identifying integer "401" will be printed at the left of each line of basic output. Plus sign specifies fourth-order integration.

0003. A rotating central body has been specified. The appropriate Martian rotation rate is entered in location 2520 via the Extra Inputs below.

ROCKET TRAJECTORY PROGRAM—INPUT FORM

DESCRIPTIVE REMARKS

2460	MARTIAN RENDEZVOUS - SEARCH FOR MAXIMUM PAYLOAD RATIO
2470	
2480	J. DOE SEPT. 29, 1962
2490	
0000	(A)

INITIAL CONDITIONS

	SEQUENCE NO.	OBLAT.	ROTAT.	INCON.	
0001	+401 +03	+1	+01 +2 +01	+01	////
	TIME	ALT.	LAT.	LONG.	VEL.
0005					
	GAMMA	AZIM.	WGT.	LAUNCH LAT.	LAUNCH LONG.
0010	+9	+02 +1	+91		
	INER. REF. LONG.	ALPHA	BETA	N BODY	
0015					
	NO. TRACKERS	LAT. T1	LONG. T1	ALT. T1	LAT. T2
0020					
	LONG. T2	ALT. T2	LAT. T3	LONG. T3	ALT. T3
0025					

SECTION CONDITIONS

	TERMINATION COND.	TERM V1	TERM V2	TERM V3	TERM V4
0100	+4 +91 +23 +02				
0200	-1 +02 +1 +03				
0300					
0400					

	JETT. WGT.	TILT ANGLE	REF. AREA	THRUST COEF	F.F. COEF.
0105			+15 -02		
0205		+1 +00	+15 -02		
0305					
0405					

	AERO. COEF.	GUID. COEF.	EX. COEF.		
0110					
0210					
0310					
0410					

	MULT. VAL. FLAG.	V1	V2	V3	V4
0115					
0215	-1 +91	+5 +91			
0315					
0415					

	PRINT INTERVAL	AERO. P.O.	TRACKER P.O.	ORBIT P.O.	GUID. P.Q.
0120	+4 +91				
0220	+8 +91			+4 +03	
0320					
0420					

	SPEC. P.O.1	SPEC. P.O.2	SPEC. P.O.3	ALT. T.C.	ALT. T.V.
0125					
0225					
0325					
0425					

	THR. TABLES	AERO. TABLES	GUID. TABLES	EX. TABLES	
0130					
0230					
0330					
0430					

			EXTRA INPUTS		
2515	+1230 +02				
2500	+1109 +08	+1825 +94	+1199 +95		
2510	+1513 +16				
2520	+7058 +04	+2328 -03		+1596 -94	
0000	(A)				

(A) : ALWAYS KEYPUNCH THIS CARD

Fig. 28- Flight Control Form: Martian Rendezvous

0004.   Launch latitude is geocentric; initial
        velocity is "earth-referenced" (in this case,
        Mars-referenced).

0006-   Launch at "sea level" on Martian equator
0008.   at zero longitude.

0011.   Eastward launch.

0012.   Initial weight of vehicle = 1 lb. By scaling
        all the vehicle parameters with respect to
        this unit weight, results relative to initial
        weight are obtained which are then valid for
        any initial weight which might be considered.

0100.   Terminate Section 1 by velocity (termination
        quantity number 4, Table II).

0101.   Terminate Section 1 when v_E = 25 ft/sec.

0107.   Reference area of vehicle A_{ref} = .0015 ft^2
        during Section 1 (this is actually reference-
        area-to-initial-weight ratio).

0120.   Print every four seconds during Section 1.

0200.   Terminate second section by extrapolated
        apogee altitude h_A (termination quantity
        number 10, Table II). Use parabolic inter-
        polation to determine endpoint (minus sign).

0201.   Terminate second section when h_A = 100 n mi.

0206.   Lower bound of tilt angle interval in which
        tilt angle producing maximum final weight is
        being sought = $0°.1$.

0215.   Iteration on an end condition during this
        section. When section termination condition
        has been reached, transfer control to the
        subroutine ITER8.

0216.   Upper bound of tilt angle interval = $5°$.

0220.   Print every eight seconds during Section 2.

0223.   Print extra orbital output. Also compute
        and print orbit circularization quantities,

including final vehicle weight w_{FC} which would remain if the vehicle were to coast to apogee and then be accelerated to circular velocity by a rocket engine with $I_{SP} = 400$ sec.

2500, 2510, 2515, 2520.   These Extra Inputs entries are used to replace the nominal earth-based program constants with Mars-based constants.[2]   By referring to the location numbers of constants, shown in Table VI (p. 198), we see that the trajectories will be run with

$r_o = a_E = .1109 \cdot 10^0$ ft $= 1825$ n mi

$\mu = .1513 \cdot 10^{16}$ ft^3/sec^2

$g_o = 12.30$ ft/sec^2

$\omega_E = .7088 \cdot 10^{-4}$ rad/sec

$\beta_A = .1596 \cdot 10^{-4}$ ft^{-1}

$\rho_{SL} = .2328 \cdot 10^{-3}$ slug/ft^3.

Upon receiving this input and being put in control of the computer, ROCKET runs the first section in a vertical trajectory until the velocity reaches 25 ft/sec. It then tries a tilt angle Θ_T of $0°.1$ and runs the second section until the extrapolated apogee altitude reaches 100 n mi, at which point it computes that the weight remaining in a circular orbit at 100 n mi would be $w_{FC} = .0353$ (with respect to the unit takeoff weight). It then returns and reruns the second section using $\Theta_T = 5°$ and obtains $w_{FC} = .0464$. The second section is then run six more times, with ROCKET conducting a Fibonaccian search for the tilt angle producing the maximum final weight in orbit. The successive values of Θ_T and the corresponding values of w_{FC} are:

Iteration	3	4	5	6	7	8
Θ_T	1.97	3.13	3.84	4.29	3.57	4.01
w_{FC}	.0446	.0481	.0498	.0486	.0487	.0507

At the end of the run, then, it has been found that the optimum tilt angle lies in the range $[3^{\circ}.84, 4^{\circ}.29]$, and that the value $\Theta_T = 4^{\circ}.01$ is certainly optimal to within $0^{\circ}.28$. For $\Theta_T = 4^{\circ}.01$, final weight in a 100-n mi circular orbit is 5.07% of the takeoff weight, and the corresponding thrust cutoff conditions are $h_E = 117,050$ ft, $v_E = 4584$ ft/sec, $\gamma = 39^{\circ}.3$, and $w = 0.22$, or 22% of the takeoff weight.

Chapter 5

OUTPUT

A.   OUTPUT CONTROL

Output from the ROCKET program appears in the following order:

1.   ***ROCKET***

2.   Run description

3.   ***PROGRAM INPUT***

4.   Nonzero Initial Conditions with position number on input form (Section O)

5.   Nonzero Section Conditions with section number and position number on input form

6.   Table descriptions

7.   Output for Section 1, Branch 1

    7a.   Headings (quantities to be printed and units)

    7b.   Values at start of branch

          $\vdots$

    7i.   Values at output point t_{PO}

          $\vdots$

    7m.   Values at end of branch

8.   Output for Section 1, Branch 2

          $\vdots$

All output is printed in a standard eight-digit floating decimal form described in Appendix E.   Figures

29 and 30 are the first two pages of output from Example
1 of Chap. 4, showing items 1 through part of item 7 of
the output. Compare Fig. 29 with the input for Example
1, shown in Fig. 17 (p. 74).

The amount of time Δt_{PO}, in seconds, between
successive output points in each branch of a section is
specified by the user in location --20 of the Section
Conditions on the input form (see Appendix A, Sec. 2).
The number of quantities printed at each output point in
a section is also controlled by the user, by means of
locations --21 through --27 of the Section Conditions.

The quantities which the ROCKET program can print out
have been divided into three general categories:

1. Quantities of greatest general interest. These
   comprise the basic output, which is printed at
   every output point; they are described in
   Sec. B below.

2. Quantities of lesser general interest. These
   are divided into four categories; the quantities
   in each category will be printed out during a
   section only if the user calls for them on the
   input form. Quantities in the aerodynamics
   category are enumerated in Sec. C; Sec.
   D describes the optional tracking output
   quantities; Sec. E, the optional orbital

```
                                                                        **   XXXXXXXXXXXXXXXXXXXXXXXX****
*** R O C K E T ***            *          *          **       ****   *XXXXXXXXXXXXXXXXXXXXXXXXXXXXXXX**
                                                                        **   XXXXXXXXXXXXXXXXXXXXXXXX****
```

SPUTSPUT I FLIGHT TEST
J. JONES JAN. 2, 1963

PROGRAM INPUT

SEC	POS	VALUE	SEC	POS	VALUE	SEC	POS	VALUE	SEC	POS	VALUE	SEC	POS	VALUE
0	1	0.10100000E 03	0	6	0.14260000E 04	0	7	0.34156200E 02	0	8	-0.11624809E 03	0	11	0.90000000E 02
0	12	0.72400000E 03	0	20	0.09999999E 01	0	21	0.34113599E 02	0	22	-0.11616749E 03	0	23	0.17380000E 04
1	0	0.20000000E 01	1	1	0.39500000E 03	1	7	0.09999999E 01	1	15	0.80000000E 01	1	16	0.95000000E 00
1	17	0.09999999E 01	1	18	0.10500000E 01	1	20	0.40000000E 01	1	22	0.09999999E 01			
2	0	-0.30000000E 01	2	7	0.09999999E 01	2	20	0.16000000E 02	2	22	0.09999999E 01			

1959 ARDC MODEL ATMOSPHERE
SPUTSPUT I LINEAR CONTROL SCHEME -- THRUST ANGLES VS TIME

Fig. 29- Input Printout: Sputsput I

SEQ	TIME (SEC)	ALT (FT)	LAT (DEG)	LONG (DEG)	VEL (FT/SEC)	GAMMA (DEG)	PSI V (DEG)	RANGE (NMI)
SEQ	WGT (LB)	AX ACCEL (G)	THRUST (LB)	FLOW (LB/SEC)	AX AERO (LB)	AL AERO (LB)	ALPHA (DEG)	DT (SEC)
T	RANGE 1 (NM)		ELEV 1 (DEG)	AZIM 1 (DEG)	RANGE 2 (NM)	ELEV 2 (DEG)	AZIM 2 (DEG)	
T	RANGE 3 (NM)	ELEV 3 (DEG)	ELEV 3 (DEG)	AZIM 3 (DEG)				

101	0.	0.14260000E 04	0.34156199E 02	-0.11624809E 02	0.	0.89999998E 02	0.89999998E 02	0.
101	0.72400000E 03	0.33964846E 01	0.24590550E 04	0.80000000E 01	0.	0.	0.	
T	0.47532069E 01		-0.66014365E 00	-0.57416642E 02				

101	0.25000000E-00	0.14284113E 04	0.34156199E 02	-0.11624809E 02	0.19303332E 02	0.89948092E 02	0.89999997E 02	0.
101	0.72200000E 03	0.34056824E 01	0.24590726E 04	0.80000000E 01	0.16985039E-00	0.	0.	0.25000000E-00
T	0.47551945E 01		-0.65617739E 00	-0.57416575E 02				

101	0.40000000E 01	0.20532620E 04	0.34156199E 02	-0.11624809E 02	0.31576619E 03	0.89762916E 02	0.90000001E 02	0.42496520E-03
101	0.69199999E 03	0.34956604E 01	0.24636137E 04	0.80000000E 01	0.44616695E 02	0.	0.	0.50000000E 00
T	0.47529109E 01		0.58330090E 00	-0.57414012E 02				

101	0.80000000E 01	0.39598972E 04	0.34156199E 02	-0.11624802E 02	0.63745308E 03	0.88643006E 02	0.90000039E 02	0.37328859E-02
101	0.65999999E 03	0.34875564E 01	0.24769574E 04	0.80000000E 01	0.17176650E 03	0.	0.	0.09999999E 01
T	0.47640932E 01		0.43607044E 01	-0.57392259E 02				

101	0.12000000E 02	0.71387610E 04	0.34156199E 02	-0.11624746E 02	0.95280907E 03	0.85508741E 02	0.90000349E 02	0.31305349E-01
101	0.62799999E 03	0.34120332E 01	0.24975453E 04	0.80000000E 01	0.34839664E 03	0.	0.	0.50000000E 00
T	0.48100212E 01		0.10607587E 02	-0.57212479E 02				

101	0.16000000E 02	0.11542792E 05	0.34156199E 02	-0.11624600E 02	0.12589630E 04	0.83301985E 02	0.90011173E 02	0.10401177E-00
101	0.59599999E 03	0.33403347E 01	0.25229389E 04	0.80000000E 01	0.53006693E 03	0.	0.	0.09999999E 01
T	0.49377645E 01		0.19033702E 02	-0.56729384E 02				

101	0.20000000E 02	0.17132414E 05	0.34156199E 02	-0.11624359E 02	0.15590458E 04	0.82060971E 02	0.90002524E 02	0.22371864E-00
101	0.56399999E 03	0.33195157E 01	0.25504167E 04	0.80000000E 01	0.67811262E 03	0.	0.	0.09999999E 01
T	0.52231273E 01		0.28976689E 02	-0.55906550E 02				

101	0.23999999E 02	0.23900005E 05	0.34156199E 02	-0.11624031E 02	0.18627982E 04	0.81269211E 02	0.90004370E 02	0.38703240E-00
101	0.53199999E 03	0.33919912E 01	0.25775287E 04	0.80000000E 01	0.76907033E 03	0.	0.	0.09999999E 01
T	0.57412052E 01		0.39403109E 02	-0.54724091E 02				

| 101 | 0.27999999E 02 | 0.31885611E 05 | 0.34156198E 02 | -0.11623607E 02 | 0.21857246E 04 | 0.80548162E 02 | 0.90006747E 02 | 0.59743144E 00 |
| 101 | 0.49999999E 03 | 0.36171047E 01 | 0.26022376E 04 | 0.80000000E 01 | 0.79360494E 03 | 0. | 0. | 0.09999999E 01 |

Fig. 30- Sample Output: Sputsput I

output quantities; and Sec. F, the optional guidance output.

3. Quantities of rare general interest. No specific provision has been made for printing these quantities; however, the user may supply and call upon three special output routines titled PSPEC1, PSPEC2, and PSPEC3, to compute and print these quantities. If the number 1 is placed in the SPEC. P.O. 1 slot (--25 on the input form) of a section, ROCKET will call upon the subroutine PSPEC1 at each output point of the section to compute and print its output quantities. The subroutines PSPEC2 and PSPEC3 are activated similarly by means of the slots SPEC. P.O. 2 and SPEC. P.O. 3 on the input form.

An example has been prepared in Fig. 31, showing the basic output, all of the optional outputs, and a special printout of the earth-referenced x, y, and z coordinates of the vehicle, obtained by coding an appropriate subroutine labeled PSPEC1 (shown below) and placing a nonzero quantity in the SPEC P.O. 1 slot for the section on the input form. The optional outputs corresponding to this figure were obtained by placing AERO P.O. = 1., TRACKER P.O. = 2., ORBIT P.O. = 300., and GUID P.O. = 1.

```
SEQ  TIME (SEC)      ALT (FT)      LAT (DEG)       LONG (DEG)      VEL (FT/SEC)      GAMMA (DEG)      PSI V (DEG)    RANGE (NMI)
SEQ  WGT (LB)        AX ACCEL (G)  THRUST (LB)     FLOW (LB/SEC)   AX AERO (LB)      AL AERO (LB)     ALPHA (DEG)    DT (SEC)

A    MACH            Q (LB/FT2)                    BT AERO (LB)    C AX              C AL             R+O V3 (BTU/FT2-SEC)
A    NORM ACCEL (G)  DV GRAV (FT/SEC)              DV DRAG (FT/SEC) AIR DENS (SL/FT3) AIR PRESS (LB/FT2)  BETA(DEG)

T 1  RANGE (NM)      ELEV (DEG)                    AZIM (DEG)                                          EL RT (RAD/SEC)  AZ RT (RAD/SEC)

O    SEMIAXIS (ERU)  ECC                           INCL (DEG)      NODE (DEG)        ARG PERI (DEG)   TR ANOM (DEG)
O    V INER (FT/SEC) GAM INER (DEG)                EGY (FT2/SEC2)  H APOG (NM)       H PERI (NM)      R IMP (NM)
O    V APOG          V C APOG        W F CIRC

G    THETA (DEG)     DEL I (DEG)     TAU AL (DEG   TAU BT (DEG)                       THETA I (DEG)    T+ DOT (RAD/SEC)

X1   X (FT)          Y (FT)          Z (FT)
```

```
975  0.62000000E 02  0.12120000E 06  0.23449999E 02 -0.79673999E 02  0.15276999E 05  0.32644797E 02  0.82430997E 02  0.29690557E 03
975  0.18860400E 06  0.66789513E 00  0.20422599E 06  0.82739999E 03  0.78257059E 05  0.35571390E 04  0.99999946E 00  0.

A    0.14693183E 02  0.17785695E 04  0.12449986E 05                  0.44000000E-00  0.20000000E-00                  0.69848858E 05
A    0.69785827E-01  0.              0.              0.              0.15241395E-04  0.11769039E 02  0.
T    0.29853059E 03  0.15041176E 01  0.17117448E 03  0.17193225E 00  0.11253838E 04  0.45019684E-02    -0.70930064E-02
O    0.63110610E 00  0.71793225E 00  0.24368830E 02 -0.15267787E 03 -0.91160490E 02  0.16584134E 03
O    0.16469874E 05  0.30023801E 02 -0.53354014E 09  0.28964625E 03 -0.28276961E 04  0.13875238E 04
O    0.13236472E 05  0.24922726E 05  0.56199895E 05
G    0.33644797E 02  0.49450684E 01  0.20000000E-00  0.            0.28699729E 02                   0.20943950E-02
X1   0.34592038E 07 -0.18985789E 08  0.83711434E 07
```

```
975  0.62249999E 02  0.12326074E 06  0.23451153E 02 -0.79664534E 02  0.15278232E 05  0.32631450E 02  0.82433211E 02  0.29691482E 03
975  0.18839715E 06  0.70271216E 00  0.20422599E 06  0.82739999E 03  0.71829543E 05  0.32649792E 04  0.10435302E 01  0.25000000E-00

A    0.14694369F 02  0.16324896E 04  0.11427427E 05                  0.44000000E-00  0.20000000E-00                  0.64117111E 05
A    0.64225872E-01  0.42887506E 01  0.32001762E 01  0.13987309E-04  0.10800654E 02  0.
T    0.29857750E 03  0.15685767E 01  0.17107289E 03  0.15660778E 04  0.44978792E-02    -0.70938332E-02
O    0.63121298E 00  0.71777709E 00  0.24369431E 02 -0.15267254E 03 -0.91152053E 02  0.16583776E 03
O    0.16471381E 05  0.30011402E 02 -0.53344981E 09  0.28994100E 03 -0.28272555E 04  0.13888215E 04
O    0.13239589E 05  0.24921741E 05  0.56162120E 05
G    0.33675081E 02  0.49453516E 01  0.20000000E-00  0.            0.28729729E 02                   0.20943950E-02
X1   0.34626488E 07 -0.18986910F 08  0.83723517E 07
```

```
975  0.63000000F 02  0.12944049E 06  0.23454612E 02 -0.79636127E 02  0.15283476E 05  0.32591391E 02  0.82440906E 02  0.29694600E 03
975  0.18777660E 06  0.79160246E 00  0.20422599E 06  0.82739999E 03  0.55561613E 05  0.25255278E 04  0.11745674E 01  0.25000000E-00

A    0.14699412E 02  0.12627639E 04  0.88393475E 04                  0.44000000E-00  0.20000000E-00                  0.49512910E 05
A    0.50133349E-01  0.17140605E 02  0.11326434E 02  0.10812046E-04  0.83488026E 01  0.
T    0.29872608E 03  0.17615850E 01  0.17076799E 03  0.12505985E 04  0.44857350E-02    -0.70958634E-02
O    0.63156385E 00  0.71726558E 00  0.24371008E 02 -0.15265860E 03 -0.91121177E 02  0.16582333E 03
O    0.16477449E 05  0.29974431E 02 -0.53315344E 09  0.29090306E 03 -0.28258035E 04  0.13930682E 04
O    0.13249873E 05  0.24918527E 05  0.56055460E 05
G    0.33766059E 02  0.49463308E 01  0.20000000E-00  0.            0.28819728E 02                   0.20943950E-02
X1   0.34729903E 07 -0.18990267F 08  0.83759756E 07
```

```
975  0.63999999E 02  0.13767350E 06  0.23459223E 02 -0.79598225E 02  0.15293387E 05  0.32538080E 02  0.82453140E 02  0.29700046E 03
975  0.18694919E 06  0.88108367E 00  0.20422599E 06  0.82739999E 03  0.39478157E 05  0.17944617E 04  0.13454424E 01  0.25000000E-00
```

Fig. 31- ROCKET Output Options

The effects of these settings are explained in the remaining sections of this chapter, which describe in detail the basic output and the various optional outputs.

The subroutine PSPEC1 which produced the printout of the x, y, z coordinates is given here as an example:

```
        SUBRØUTINE PSPEC1
        (COMMON package)
        IF (ØUT1) 2,2,1
1       WRITE ØUTPUT TAPE 6,4
        GØ TØ 3
2       CALL DELE
        WRITE ØUTPUT TAPE 6,5, (RXYZG(I), I = 1, 3)
3       RETURN
4       FØRMAT (45H0X1    X(FT)(13) Y(FT)(13) Z(FT))
5       FØRMAT (3H X1 3E18.8)
        END
```

Comments:

The use of the COMMON package is explained in Appendix E, Sec. 5.

ØUT1 is a flag which is equal to 1 when ROCKET is printing headings, and zero otherwise.

WRITE ØUTPUT TAPE 6 is the form in which ROCKET output statements are written (see Appendix E).

DELE is a subroutine which computes x, y, and z,

placing them in the locations RXYZG (1), (2), (3).

The subscripted (13) stands for 13 blanks.

B. BASIC OUTPUT

The following quantities are printed as basic output:

Sequence number, a three-digit integer, obtained from location 1 of the Flight Control Form, which is used to identify the run.

Time t (sec).

Altitude h_E of vehicle above sea level (ft).

Latitude ϕ (deg).

Longitude λ (deg).

Earth-referenced velocity v_E (ft/sec).

Flight path angle γ (deg).

Velocity azimuth angle Ψ_v (deg).

Surface range R_S (n mi).

Weight w (lb).

Axial acceleration $\left[T_A + A_A + X_A \right] / w$ (g).

Thrust T (lb).

Fuel flow $-\dot{w}$ (lb/sec).

Axial aerodynamic force $-A_A$ (lb).

A1-axis aerodynamic force A_{A1} (lb).

Angle of attack α (deg).

Integration stepsize Δt (sec).

C. AERODYNAMIC OUTPUT

The following quantities constitute the optional aerodynamic output obtained during a section by placing a nonzero quantity in the section's AERO P.O. slot on the Flight Control Form:

Mach number M.

Dynamic pressure q (lb/ft^2).

B-axis aerodynamic force A_B (lb).

Axial force coefficient C_A.

Al-axis force coefficient C_{A1}.

Heating parameter $\rho_A \cdot v_E^3/778$ (BTU/ft^2 - sec).

Normal acceleration $\sqrt{F_B^2 + F_{A1}^2}/w$ (g).

Velocity loss due to gravity Δv_G (ft/sec).

Velocity loss due to drag Δv_D (ft/sec).

Atmospheric density ρ_A ($slug/ft^3$).

Atmospheric pressure P_A (lb/ft^2).

Sideslip angle β (deg).

The quantities Δv_G and Δv_D are obtained from

$$\Delta v_G = \int_{t_o}^{t} \frac{\mu}{r^2} \sin \gamma \, dt \qquad (5\text{-}13)$$

$$\Delta v_D = \int_{t_o}^{t} \frac{A_A \cos \alpha \cos \beta - A_{A1} \sin \alpha \cos \beta - A_B \sin \beta) \cdot g_o}{w} \, dt. \qquad (5\text{-}14)$$

D. TRACKING OUTPUT

Coordinates of as many as three tracking stations can be entered in the Initial Conditions block of the input form. On request the program prints out tracking data from as many tracking stations as have been entered. If the number placed in the TRACKER P.O. slot during a section is equal to 1., the program will print out for each station the quantities:

ρ_T, the straight-line range from tracking station to vehicle (n mi);

Θ_E, the elevation angle, or angle the vehicle makes with the local horizontal at the tracking station (deg);

Θ_A, the azimuth angle of the vehicle as seen from the tracking station, measured eastward from north (deg).

If the number placed in the TRACKER P.O. slot during a section is greater than 1., the program will also print out for each station the time derivatives of the basic tracking quantities:

$\dot{\rho}_T$, the range rate (ft/sec);

$\dot{\Theta}_E$, the elevation rate (rad/sec);

$\dot{\Theta}_A$, the azimuth rate (rad/sec).

Equations (B-47), p. 171 of Appendix B, are used to transform the position vector $\bar{r}$ of the vehicle into the earth-referenced (x_G, y_G, z_G) system (Fig. 39, p. 172), via the subroutine DELE.

The rotation matrix $M_1^{-1}(\lambda_T, \phi_T)$ then transforms $\bar{r}$ into a tracker-oriented (x_T, y_T, z_T) system (see Fig. 32).

The quantity $(r_{x_T} - R_T)$, where $R_T = r_E + h_T$ (earth radius plus tracker altitude), represents the upward component of the vehicle's position vector with respect to the tracking station; r_{y_T} represents the eastward component, and r_{z_T} the northward component. Thus we have:

$$\rho_T = \left[(r_{x_T}^2 - R_T)^2 + r_{y_T}^2 + r_{z_T}^2 \right]^{\frac{1}{2}} \qquad (5\text{-}15)$$

$$\Theta_E = \tan^{-1} \frac{r_{x_T} - R_T}{(r_{y_T}^2 + r_{z_T}^2)^{\frac{1}{2}}} \qquad (5\text{-}16)$$

$$\Theta_A = \tan^{-1} (r_{y_T}/r_{z_T}). \qquad (5\text{-}17)$$

To find the tracking rates, we first express the velocity vector $\bar{v} = \dot{\bar{r}}$ in the local (R, L, P) system by Eqs. (3-12) (p. 54). We then apply the rotation matrix $M_1(\lambda, \phi)$ to $\bar{v}$, to express $\bar{v}$ in the earth-referenced (x_G, y_G, z_G)

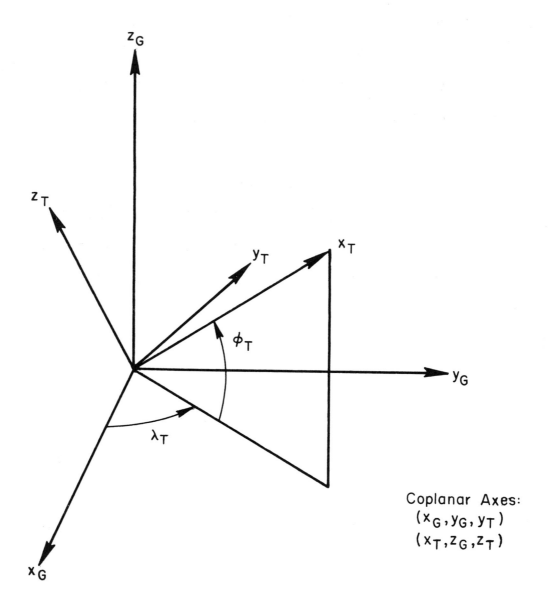

Coplanar Axes:
(x_G, y_G, y_T)
(x_T, z_G, z_T)

Fig. 32- Tracker Coordinates

system. The matrix $M_1^{-1}(\lambda_T, \phi_T)$ then transforms $\bar{v}$ into the local tracker-oriented (x_T, y_T, z_T) system, and another matrix $M_3(\Theta_A, \Theta_E)$ then carries $\bar{v}$ into a tracker-to-vehicle oriented (x_ρ, y_ρ, z_ρ) system with x_ρ in the direction of increasing range ρ_T; y_ρ in the direction of increasing elevation Θ_E; and z_ρ in the direction of increasing azimuth Θ_A (see Fig. 33). The total transformation is:

$$\begin{pmatrix} v_{x_\rho} \\ v_{y_\rho} \\ v_{z_\rho} \end{pmatrix} = M_3(\Theta_A, \Theta_E) \cdot M_1^{-1}(\lambda_T, \phi_T) \cdot M_1(\lambda, \phi) \begin{pmatrix} v_R \\ v_L \\ v_P \end{pmatrix} ,$$

where

$$M_3(\Theta_A, \Theta_E) = \begin{pmatrix} \sin \Theta_E & \cos \Theta_E \sin \Theta_A & \cos \Theta_E \cos \Theta_A \\ \cos \Theta_E & -\sin \Theta_E \sin \Theta_A & -\sin \Theta_E \cos \Theta_A \\ 0 & \cos \Theta_A & -\sin \Theta_A \end{pmatrix} .$$

$$(5\text{-}18)$$

The tracking rates are then obtained from the formulas:

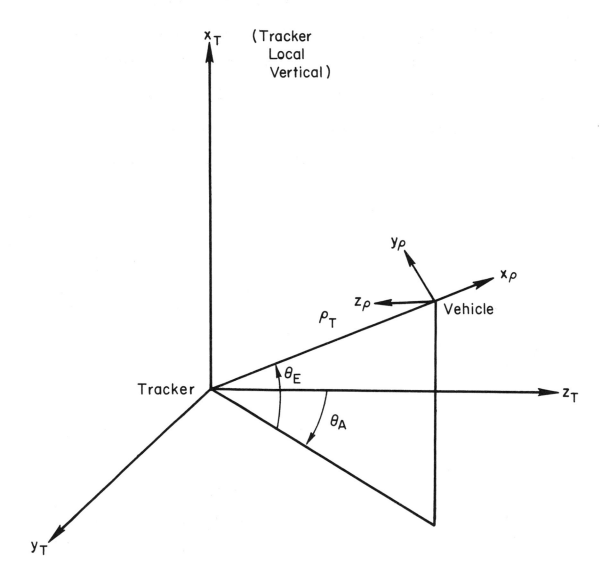

Fig. 33- Tracker-to-Vehicle Coordinates

$$\dot{\rho}_T = v_{x_\rho}$$

$$\dot{\Theta}_E = v_{y_\rho}/\rho_T$$

$$\dot{\Theta}_A = v_{z_\rho}/\rho_T \cos \Theta_E. \qquad (5\text{-}19)$$

E. ORBITAL OUTPUT

Basic Orbital Quantities

At each point along the trajectory, the vehicle's position and velocity determine a conic section which represents the path the vehicle would follow if the only force acting on it were an unperturbed inverse-square gravitational force. The elements of this osculating orbit and some associated quantities are printed during a section if the number 1. is placed in the section's ORBIT P.O. slot on the input form.

Semi-major axis a of osculating orbit (eru)

Eccentricity e of osculating orbit

Inclination i with respect to equator (deg)

Inertial longitude of node Ω (deg)

Argument of perigee ω_P (deg)

True anomaly v_P (deg)

Inertial velocity v_I (ft/sec)

Inertial flight path angle γ_I (deg)

Energy per unit mass EGY (ft^2/sec^2)

Apogee altitude h_A (n mi)

Perigee altitude h_P (n mi)

Surface range R_{IMP} between launch point and
   ballistic impact point (n mi)

A geometrical picture of the orbit and its elements
is given in Fig. 34. The subroutine EXTRAP (pp. 173-176)
is used to compute the quantities v_I, γ_I, EGY, $\dot{r}r$, P, a,
e, h_A, and R_{IMP}. The unit vector $\bar{N}$ normal to the orbital
plane is then obtained by

$$\bar{N} = \frac{\bar{r} \times \dot{\bar{r}}}{|\bar{r} \times \dot{\bar{r}}|} . \tag{5-20}$$

If $|\bar{r} \times \dot{\bar{r}}| = 0$, then i, Ω, ω_P, and v_P are set to zero; if
not,

$$i = \cos^{-1}(N_{z_I}). \tag{5-21}$$

If i = 0, then Ω and ω_P are set to zero; if not,

$$\Omega = \tan^{-1}(N_{x_I}/-N_{y_I}) \tag{5-22}$$

$$\tan u = \frac{r_{z_I}}{\sin i \, (r_{x_I} \cos \Omega + r_{y_I} \sin \Omega)} . \tag{5-23}$$

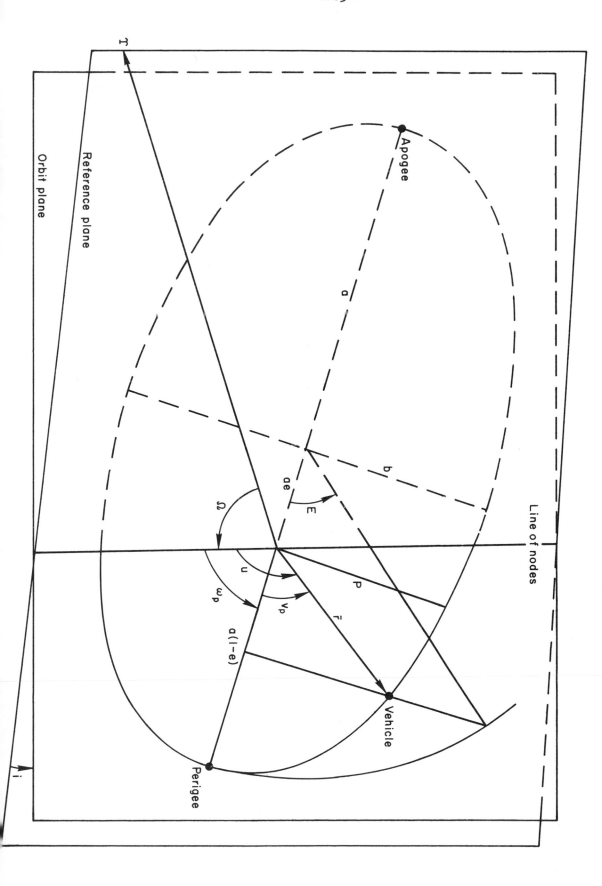

Fig. 34- Orbit Geometry

If $e = 0$, then ω_P and v_P are set to zero. If EGY > 0, the orbit is a hyperbola, and ω_P, v_P, h_P, h_A, and R_{IMP} are set to zero. If EGY < 0, the orbit is an ellipse, with

$$e \cos E = 1 - \frac{r}{a} \tag{5-24}$$

$$e \sin E = \frac{r\dot{r}}{\sqrt{\mu a}} \tag{5-25}$$

$$v_P = \tan^{-1} \left(\frac{\sqrt{1-e^2}\; e \sin E}{e \cos E - e^2} \right) \tag{5-26}$$

$$\omega_P = u - v_P \tag{5-27}$$

$$h_P = a(1-e) - r_o. \tag{5-28}$$

Orbit Circularization Quantities

The orbital printout option is also capable of calculating and printing some handy quantities concerning orbit circularization. If the number in the ORBIT P.O. slot on the input form is greater than 1., it is interpreted as the specific impulse I_{SP} of a rocket engine. The program then computes and prints v_A, the inertial velocity at the apogee of the osculating orbit; v_C, the circular velocity at apogee; and w_{FC}, the final vehicle weight which would remain if the vehicle were to coast to apogee and then be accelerated (instantaneously) to circular velocity by the rocket engine; using

$$v_A = \sqrt{\frac{\mu(1 - e)}{a(1 + e)}}$$

$$v_C = \sqrt{\frac{\mu}{a(1 + e)}} \qquad\qquad (5\text{-}29)$$

$$w_{FC} = w \cdot \exp\left(\frac{v_A - v_C}{g_o I_{SP}}\right)$$

where w is the current weight of the vehicle, and a and e are the osculating semi-major axis and eccentricity.

F. GUIDANCE OUTPUT

Guidance schemes tend to vary more from mission to mission than do the methods for determining aerodynamic and propulsion effects. The present list of guidance quantities to be printed, representing quantities common to a number of guidance schemes, is thus a small one; other quantities can be added to or substituted into the list as desired. At present, the following quantities are printed during a section if a nonzero quantity is placed in the section's GUID P.O. slot on the input form:

Vehicle attitude angle Θ (deg);

Inertial range angle Δ_I (deg);

Thrust angle τ_α (deg);

Thrust angle τ_β (deg);

Vehicle inertial attitude angle Θ_I (deg);

Attitude angle rate ($\dot{\Theta}$ or $\dot{\Theta}_I$) (deg/sec).

The attitude angle rate will appear as zero unless it is being used specifically in a program to calculate Θ or Θ_I by integration.

Appendix A
FLIGHT CONTROL FORM CATALOGUE

1. INITIAL CONDITIONS

LOCATION	TITLE	COMMENTS
2460-2490	COMMENTS	A description of the run, printed out at the beginning of the output.
0001	SEQUENCE NO.	The absolute value of this integer, less than 1000, is printed as run identification with each line of basic output. Also used to specify integration method: if ≥ 0, use 4-point integration; if < 0, use 2-point integration.
0002	OBLAT.	If = 0, use spherical earth model; if ≠ 0, use oblate earth model.
0003	ROTAT.	If = 0, use nonrotating earth model; if ≠ 0, use rotating earth model.
0004	INCON.	Indicates form in which initial position and velocity are expressed in locations 0006-0011.

LOCATION	TITLE	COMMENTS

If = 0, use geodetic latitude and earth-referenced velocity for Initial Conditions 0007, 0009;

if = 1, use geodetic latitude and inertial velocity;

if = 2, use geocentric latitude and earth-referenced velocity;

if = 3, use geocentric latitude and inertial velocity;

if = 4, interpret locations 0006-0011 as Initial Conditions in terms of inertial x,y,z in eru, and $\dot{x},\dot{y},\dot{z}$ in eru/sec;

if = 5, interpret locations 0006-0011 as Initial Conditions in terms of orbital elements a (eru), e (nondim), and i, Ω, ω_p, v_p (deg).

LOCATION	TITLE	COMMENTS
0005	TIME	Time t_z of Initial Conditions (sec).

LOCATION	TITLE	COMMENTS
0006	ALT.	Initial altitude h_E above sea level (ft).
0007	LAT.	Initial latitude ϕ (deg).
0008	LONG.	Initial longitude λ (deg).
0009	VEL.	Initial velocity v (ft/sec).
0010	GAMMA	Initial flight path angle γ (deg).
0011	AZIM.	Initial azimuth angle Ψ_V (deg).
0012	WGT.	Initial weight w (lb).
0013	LAUNCH LAT.	If = 0, use 0007 as launch latitude ϕ_K (deg), 0008 as launch longitude λ_K (deg); if $\neq$ 0, use 0013 as launch latitude ϕ_K (deg), geodetic or geocentric according to initial latitude ϕ (see 0004), 0014 as launch longitude λ_K (deg).
0014	LAUNCH LONG.	See above.
0015	INER. REF. LONG.	Inertial longitude λ_{G_o} of Greenwich prime meridian at $t = 0$ (deg).
0016	ALPHA	Initial angle of attack α (deg).
0017	BETA	Initial sideslip angle β (deg).

LOCATION	TITLE	COMMENTS
0018	N BODY	If = 0, no special action; if = 1, compute lunar accelerations (see Appendix D); if = 2, compute solar accelerations; if = 3, compute lunar and solar accelerations.
0020	NO. TRACKERS	Number of tracking stations (trackers).
0021	LAT. T1	Latitude ϕ_{T1} of tracker 1 (deg), geodetic or geocentric according to initial latitude ϕ (see 0004).
0022	LONG. T1	Longitude λ_{T1} of tracker 1 (deg).
0023	ALT. T1	Altitude $h_{E_{T1}}$ of tracker 1 above sea level (ft).
0024	LAT. T2	Latitude ϕ_{T2} of tracker 2 (deg).
0025	LONG. T2	Longitude λ_{T2} of tracker 2 (deg).
0026	ALT. T2	Altitude $h_{E_{T2}}$ of tracker 2 (ft).
0027	LAT. T3	Latitude ϕ_{T3} of tracker 3 (deg).
0028	LONG. T3	Longitude λ_{T3} of tracker 3 (deg).
0029	ALT. T3	Altitude $h_{E_{T3}}$ of tracker 3 (ft).
0030-0099		Available for use via the program symbols B(30)-B(99).

2. SECTION CONDITIONS

LOCATION (Modulo 100)	TITLE	COMMENTS
0	TERM. COND.	Termination condition flag (see Chap. 2, Sec. C).
1-4	TERM. V1-V4	Termination values (see Chap. 2, Sec. C).
5	JETT. WGT.	Jettison weight w_J (lb). If $w_J > 0$, w_J is subtracted from the vehicle's weight at the beginning of the section; if $w_J < 0$, the vehicle's weight at the beginning of the section is set equal to $|w_J|$.
6	TILT ANGLE	Tilt angle θ_T (deg). Flight path angle γ is instantaneously diminished by this angle at the beginning of section. Vehicle speed unchanged.
7	REF. AREA	Vehicle reference area A_{ref} (ft^2), used in aerodynamics calculations.

LOCATION (Modulo 100)	TITLE	COMMENTS
8	THRUST COEF.	A multiplicative constant C_T which is applied to thrust forces (specified via the Flight Programming Form). If left blank or zero, C_T is set to unity.
9	F.F. COEF.	A multiplicative constant C_{FF} which is applied to the fuel flow. If left blank or zero, C_{FF} is set to unity.
10	AERO. COEF.	A multiplicative constant C_{AERO} which is applied to aerodynamic forces. If left blank or zero, C_{AERO} is set to unity.
11	GUID. COEF.	A multiplicative constant C_{GUID} which is applied to guidance angles. If left blank or zero, C_{GUID} is set to unity.
12	EX. COEF.	An extra multiplicative constant C_{EX} which is at the disposal of the user. If left blank or zero, C_{EX} is set to unity.

LOCATION (Modulo 100)	TITLE	COMMENTS
15	MULT. VAL. FLAG	Multiple value flag or iteration indicator (see Chap. 2, Secs. D and E).
16-19	V1-V4	Multiple values 1-4 (see Chap. 2, Secs. D and E).
20	PRINT INTERVAL	Interval Δt_{ro} at which printout occurs (sec). This number should always be some integral power of 2.
21	AERO P.O.	If = 0, do not print aerodynamic data; if $\neq$ 0, print aerodynamic data.
22	TRACKER P.O.	If = 0, do not print tracking data; if = 1, print tracking coordinates; if $\geq$ 2, print tracking coordinates and rates.
23	ORBIT P.O.	If = 0, do not print orbital data; if = 1, print orbital data;

LOCATION (Modulo 100)	TITLE	COMMENTS
		if > 1, interpret as the specific impulse I_{SP} of a rocket engine; print orbit circularization quantities (see Chap. 5, Sec. E).
24	GUID P.O.	If = 0, do not print guidance data; if $\neq$ 0, print guidance data.
25	SPEC P.O. 1	If $\neq$ 0, use special print routine 1 (see Chap. 5).
26	SPEC P.O. 2	If $\neq$ 0, use special print routine 2.
27	SPEC P.O. 3	If $\neq$ 0, use special print routine 3.
28	ALT. T.C.	Alternate termination condition flag (see Chap. 2, Sec. C).
29	ALT. T.V.	Alternate termination value (see Chap. 2, Sec. C).
30	THR. TABLES	Stage number for thrust tables. Specifies which thrust table is to be used throughout section (see Appendix C).

LOCATION (Modulo 100)	TITLE	COMMENTS
31	AERO. TABLES	Stage number for aerodynamic tables.
32	GUID. TABLES	Stage number for guidance tables.
33	EX. TABLES	Stage number for other tables.
34-99		Available for use via the program symbols H(35)-H(100).

3. GENERAL COMMENTS

1. Entries that are left blank are treated as zeros during the first run. In later runs, a blank entry retains the value assigned to it on the previous run. Entries that are left blank should not be keypunched.

2. Certain entries whose nominal value is unity (THRUST COEF., F.F. COEF., AERO. COEF., GUID. COEF., EX. COEF., THR. TABLES, AERO. TABLES, GUID. TABLES, EX. TABLES) are automatically set to unity by the program unless a nonzero quantity has been entered in them. Thus, a user desiring nominal values of these quantities may leave the entries blank.

3. Earth radius units (eru) are measured with reference to the radius r_o of the spherical earth model (Table VI, p. 198).

Appendix B
CATALOGUE OF COMPUTATIONAL SUBROUTINES

1. PROPULSION SUBROUTINES

Thrust Vectoring

Non-axial thrust forces may be specified by means of two angles, τ_α and τ_β, which relate the thrust vector to the vehicle axes (A,B,A1) as in Fig. 35.

The resultant forces along the vehicle axes are

$$T_A = T \cos \tau_\alpha \cos \tau_\beta$$

$$T_B = T \cos \tau_\alpha \sin \tau_\beta \qquad (B-30)$$

$$T_{A1} = T \sin \tau_\alpha$$

where T is the magnitude of the thrust vector.

Subroutines

CØNTAU (TA, TB) -- Constant Thrust Angles.

Inputs: THRUST, total thrust T (lb).

Outputs: TAX, thrust along A-axis T_A (lb);

TBT, thrust along B-axis T_B (lb);

TAL, thrust along A1-axis T_{A1} (lb).

Action: TA and TB are assumed to be the angles τ_α and τ_β, in degrees. They are converted to radians and used in Eq. (B-30) to produce the final T_A, T_B, and T_{A1}.

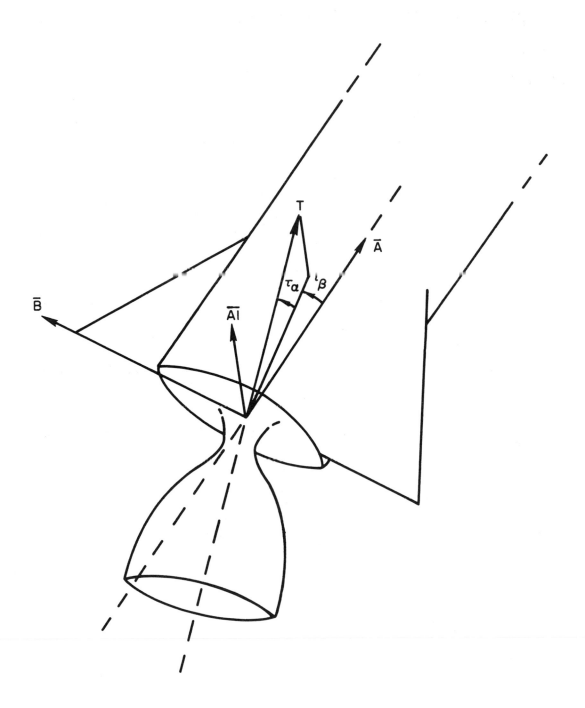

Fig. 35- Thrust Orientation

CONTFL (TH, FL) -- Constant Thrust and Fuel Flow.

Inputs: None

Outputs: THRUST, total thrust T (lb);

TAX, axial thrust T_A (lb);

WD, weight derivative $\dot{w}$ (lb/sec).

Action: TH, after being modified by the multiplicative

factor C_T, is assumed to be the thrust T in lb;

FL, after being modified by the multiplicative

factor C_{FF}, is assumed to be the fuel flow rate

in lb/sec, a positive quantity. It becomes $\dot{w}$

by a change of sign. T_A is set equal to T; thus,

all thrust will be axial unless modified by a

thrust angle subroutine.

CTAISP (TH, SPI, AE) -- Constant Vacuum Thrust and

I_{SP}; Thrust Modified by

Air Pressure.

Inputs: APRES, air pressure P_A (lb/ft^2).

Outputs: THRUST, total thrust T (lb);

TAX, axial thrust T_A (lb);

WD, weight derivative $\dot{w}$ (lb/sec).

Action: TH is assumed to be the vacuum thrust T_∞ of

the engine in lb; AE is the exit area A_E in

ft^2. T and T_A are identical and are computed

by the formula $C_T (T_\infty - A_E P_A)$, where C_T is the

optional modifying factor. The quantity SPI

is assumed to be the vacuum specific impulse

I_{SP} of the engine in sec; it is used to compute

$$\dot{w} = -C_T T_\infty / I_{SP} \ .$$

<u>CTHAIR (TH, FL, AE)</u> -- Constant Vacuum Thrust

Modified by Air Pressure.

Inputs: APRES, air pressure P_A (lb/ft^2).

Outputs: THRUST, total thrust T (lb);

TAX, axial thrust T_A (lb);

WD, weight derivative $\dot{w}$ (lb/sec).

Action: TH, after being modified by the multiplicative

factor C_T, is assumed to be the vacuum thrust

T_∞ of the engine in lb; AE is the exit area

A_E in ft^2. T and T_A are identical: T =

$T_A = T_\infty - A_E P_A$. FL, after being modified by the

multiplicative factor C_{FF}, is assumed to be

the fuel flow rate in lb/sec, a positive

quantity. It becomes $\dot{w}$ by a change of sign.

<u>TABTAU (X, N, NTB)</u> -- Tabulated Thrust Angles,

General.

Inputs: X, independent variable for the table;

THRUST, total thrust T (lb).

Outputs: TAX, thrust along A-axis T_A (lb);

TBT, thrust along B-axis T_B (lb);

TAL, thrust along A1-axis T_{A1} (lb).

Action: Tables of τ_α and τ_β, expressed in degrees, as functions of the quantity designated by X, are assumed to be located in table number NTB. A Lagrangian interpolation of order $N \leq 2$ is used to find τ_α and τ_β from X. They are then converted to radians and used in Eqs. (B-30) to produce the final T_A, T_B, and T_{A1}. If X refers to a ROCKET program variable, a COMMON package must be used when compiling (see Appendix E, Sec. 5).

TABTFL (X, N) -- Tabulated Thrust and Fuel Flow.

Inputs: X, independent variable for the table.

Outputs: THRUST, total thrust T (lb);

TAX, axial thrust T_A (lb);

WD, weight derivative $\dot{w}$ (lb/sec).

Action: Tables of T, the total thrust in lb, and FF, the positive fuel flow in lb/sec, as functions of the quantity designated by X, are assumed to be located in table number 2. A Lagrangian interpolation of order $N \leq 2$ is used to find T and FF from X. FF, after being modified by the multiplicative factor C_{FF}, is made into $\dot{w}$ by a change of sign, and T is modified by the multiplicative factor C_T. If X refers to a ROCKET program variable,

a COMMON package must be used when compiling
(see Appendix E, Sec. 5). T_A is set equal to T.

<u>TBTATM (NTB, N)</u> -- Tabulated Thrust Angles vs. Time.

Inputs: THRUST, total thrust T (lb).

Outputs: TAX, thrust along A-axis T_A (lb);

            TBT, thrust along B-axis T_B (lb);

            TAL, thrust along Al-axis T_{Al} (lb).

Action: Tables of τ_α and τ_β, expressed in degrees, as

            functions of the time t in seconds, are assumed

            to be in table number NTB. The subroutine

            TABTAU (TIME, N, NTB) is then employed to find

            T_A, T_B, and T_{Al} from t and T.

<u>TBTFHE (N)</u> -- Tabulated Thrust vs. Altitude.

Inputs: None.

Outputs: THRUST, total thrust T (lb);

            TAX, axial thrust T_A (lb);

            WD, weight derivative $\dot{w}$ (lb/sec).

Action: Tables of T in lb and FF, the positive fuel

            flow in lb/sec, as functions of altitude h_E

            in feet, are assumed to be in table number 2.

            The subroutine TABTFL (ALT, N) then is used

            to produce T and $\dot{w}$ from h_E. T_A is set equal to T.

<u>TBTFTM (N)</u> -- Tabulated Thrust vs. Time.

Inputs: None.

Outputs: THRUST, total thrust T (lb);

TAX, axial thrust T_A (lb);

WD, weight derivative $\dot{w}$ (lb/sec).

Action: Tables of T in lb and FF, the positive fuel

flow in lb/sec, as functions of the time t in

seconds, are assumed to be in table number 2.

The subroutine TABTFL (TIME, N) is then used

to produce T and $\dot{w}$ from t. T_A is set equal to T.

2. AERODYNAMIC SUBROUTINES

Aerodynamic Coefficients

The dynamic pressure $q = \frac{1}{2} \rho_A v_E^2$ expresses the
kinetic energy per unit volume of the air mass directed
against the surface of a vehicle moving through an
atmosphere of density ρ_A at a relative velocity v_E. The
forces acting on a vehicle as a result of atmospheric
resistance are generally proportional to the product of
the dynamic pressure and the reference area of the
vehicle; e.g., the axial aerodynamic force $A_A \sim q\, A_{ref}$.
The associated proportionality factors, which are
generally not constants but functions of such things as
the shape, attitude, and velocity of the vehicle, are
called the vehicle's aerodynamic coefficients. Thus, the

aerodynamic forces along the vehicle's A-, B-, and Al-axes are generally computed as follows:

$$A_A = - q \cdot A_{ref} \cdot C_A \qquad \text{(B-31)}$$

$$A_B = q \cdot A_{ref} \cdot C_B \qquad \text{(B-32)}$$

$$A_{A1} = q \cdot A_{ref} \cdot C_{A1}, \qquad \text{(B-33)}$$

where C_A, C_D, and C_{A1} are the vehicle's aerodynamic coefficients. Various ways of specifying these coefficients are provided by the aerodynamic subroutines.

Normal Force, Total Angle of Attack, and Effective Roll Angle

The normal aerodynamic force A_N is a vector quantity directed orthogonally to the vehicle axis A, and located in the plane formed by the vehicle axis A and the velocity vector V. The total angle of attack α_T is measured in this plane as the angle between A and V. The effective roll angle σ_R is defined as the angle made by the intersection of the (A,V) and (B,Al) planes with the Al-axis, measured positively toward the B-axis. Figure 36 shows the geometry of the situation.

From Fig. 36 we deduce the following formulas for obtaining α_T and σ_R:

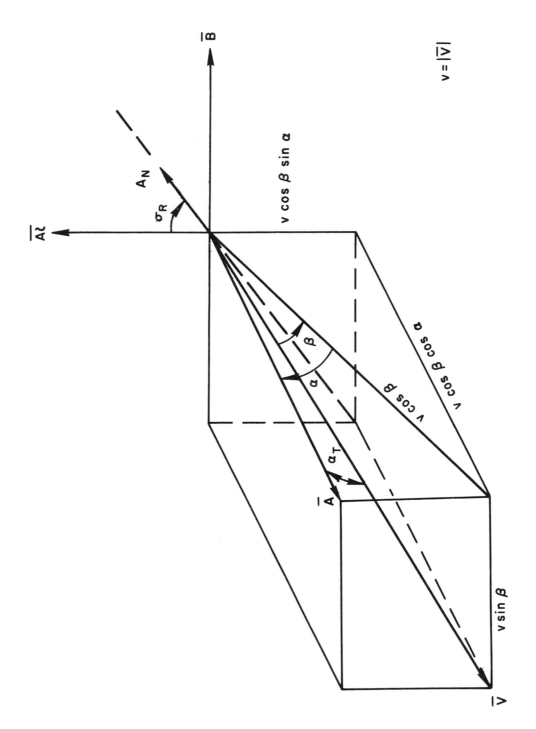

Fig. 36—Total Angle of Attack and Effective Roll Angle

$$\cos \alpha_T = \cos \alpha \cos \beta$$

$$\tan \sigma_R = \frac{\sin \beta}{\cos \beta \sin \alpha} \quad .$$

(B-34)

The normal force A_N can then be resolved along the B- and Al-axes:

$$A_B = A_N \sin \sigma_R$$

$$A_{Al} = A_N \cos \sigma_R \quad .$$

(B-35)

Subroutines

Many of these subroutines require the vehicle's reference area A_{ref} as an input. It is not a computed quantity; the user specifies it in location --07 of the Flight Control Form (see Appendix A, Sec. 2).

CALMAL (NX) -- Al-Axis Force Coefficient from Mach Number and Angle of Attack.

Inputs: EMACH, Mach number M;

ALPHAD, angle of attack α (deg);

Q, dynamic pressure q (lb/ft^2);

AREA, reference area of vehicle A_{ref} (ft^2).

Outputs: CAL, Al-axis force coefficient C_{Al};

AAL, aerodynamic force A_{Al} along Al-axis (lb).

Action: Tables of C_{A1} vs. Mach number and α in degrees
           are assumed to be in table number 17. The
           two values of the α-table which bracket α are
           chosen and two Lagrangian interpolations of
           order $NX \leq 2$ are used to find values of C_{A1}
           from M along these two lines of constant α.
           A linear interpolation in α is then used to
           find C_{A1}, which is then modified by the
           multiplicative factor C_{AERO}. A_{A1} is then
           calculated from Eq. (B-33).

   <u>CAXMAL (NX)</u> -- Axial Force Coefficient from Mach
                   Number and Angle of Attack.

Inputs: EMACH, Mach number M;
           ALPHAD, angle of attack α (deg);
           Q, dynamic pressure q (lb/ft^2);
           AREA, reference area of vehicle A_{ref} (ft^2).
Outputs: CA, axial force coefficient C_A;
           AAX, aerodynamic force A_A along A-axis (lb).
Action: The bivariate interpolation to find C_A is
           similar to that of CALMAL, except that the
           table of C_A vs. M and α is assumed to be in
           table number 16. After C_A is modified by the
           multiplicative factor C_{AERO}, A_A is determined
           by Eq. (B-31).

CBANKA (BA) -- Constant Bank Angle σ_B.

Inputs: AAL, aerodynamic force A_{A1} along A1-axis (lb).

Outputs: ABT, aerodynamic force A_B along B-axis (lb);

AAL, aerodynamic force A_{A1} along A1-axis (lb).

Action: BA is assumed to be the bank angle σ_B of the vehicle in degrees; it is modified by the multiplicative factor C_{EX} and then used to resolve the A1-axis aerodynamic force into A1 and B components:

$$A_{A1} \cos \sigma_B \longrightarrow A_{A1}$$
$$A_{A1} \sin \sigma_B \longrightarrow A_B \ .$$

(B-36)

CNMALT (NX) -- Normal Force Coefficient from Mach Number and Total Angle of Attack.

Inputs: EMACH, Mach number M;

ALPHTD, total angle of attack α_T (deg);

Q, dynamic pressure q (lb/ft^2);

AREA, reference area of vehicle A_{ref} (ft^2);

SIGR, effective roll angle σ_R (rad).

Outputs: CN, normal force coefficient C_N;

ABT, aerodynamic force A_B along B-axis (lb);

AAL, aerodynamic force A_{A1} along A1-axis (lb).

Action: Interpolation is similar to CALMAL and CAXMAL, except that α_T is used in place of α; the table of C_N vs. M and α_T is assumed to be in table number 17. After C_N is modified by the multiplicative factor C_{AERO}, the normal force A_N is computed as

$$A_N = q \cdot A_{ref} \cdot C_N . \qquad (B-37)$$

Eqs. (B-35) are then used to find A_B and A_{A1}.

CONACO (CAX, CBT, CALP) -- Constant Aerodynamic Coefficients.

Inputs: Q, dynamic pressure q (lb/ft^2);

AREA, reference area of vehicle A_{ref} (ft^2).

Outputs: CA, CB, CAL; A-, B-, and A1-axis force coefficients;

AAX, ABT, AAL; aerodynamic forces along A-, B-, and A1-axes (lb).

Action: CAX, CBT, and CALP are assumed to be C_A, C_B, and C_{A1}; their values are all modified by the multiplicative factor C_{AERO}. A_A and A_{A1} are calculated from Eqs. (B-31) and (B-33); A_B is given by Eq. (B-32).

<u>CØNCAX (CAX)</u> -- Constant Axial Force Coefficient.

Inputs: Q, dynamic pressure q (lb/ft^2);

AREA, reference area of vehicle A_{ref} (ft^2).

Outputs: CA, axial force coefficient C_A;

AAX, aerodynamic force A_A along A-axis (lb).

Action: CAX is assumed to be C_A; it is then modified

by the multiplicative factor C_{AERO}. Eq. (B-31)

is used to obtain A_A.

<u>CØNCLA (CLA)</u> -- Constant C_{A1}/α.

Inputs: ALPHAD, angle of attack α (deg);

Q, dynamic pressure q (lb/ft^2);

AREA, reference area of vehicle A_{ref} (ft^2).

Outputs: CAL, Al-axis force coefficient C_{A1};

AAL, aerodynamic force A_{A1} along Al-axis (lb).

Action: CLA is multiplied by α to obtain C_{A1}, which is

then modified by the multiplicative factor

C_{AERO}. Eq. (B-33) is used to obtain A_{A1}.

<u>CØNCNA (CNAL)</u> -- Constant C_N/α_T.

Inputs: ALPHTD, total angle of attack α_T (deg);

SIGR, effective roll angle σ_R (rad);

Q, dynamic pressure q (lb/ft^2);

AREA, reference area of vehicle A_{ref} (ft^2).

Outputs: CN, normal force coefficient C_N;

ABT, aerodynamic force A_B along B-axis (lb);

AAL, aerodynamic force A_{A1} along A1-axis (lb).

Action: CNAL is multiplied by α_T to obtain C_N, which is then modified by the coefficient C_{AERO}. Eq. (B-37) produces A_N; then A_B and A_{A1} are computed from Eqs. (B-35).

C$\emptyset$NRFA (AL$\emptyset$A) -- Constant Ratio of Aerodynamic Forces.

Inputs: AAX, aerodynamic force A_A along A-axis.

Outputs: AAL, aerodynamic force A_{A1} along A1-axis.

Action: AL$\emptyset$A is taken as A_{A1}/A_A, the ratio of normal to axial aerodynamic forces. It is modified by the multiplicative factor C_{EX}, and then A_{A1} is calculated as

$$A_{A1} = A_A \cdot (A_{A1}/A_A).$$

EXPDPQ -- Exponential Air Density and Pressure; Dynamic Pressure.

Inputs: None.

Outputs: ADENS, air density ρ_A (slug/ft^3);

APRES, air pressure P_A (lb/ft^2).

Action:

$$\rho_A = \rho_{SL}\, e^{-\beta_A h_E} \qquad (B-38)$$

$$P_A = g_o \rho_A / \beta_A \qquad (B-39)$$

$$q = \tfrac{1}{2}\rho_A \cdot v_E^2 \qquad (B-40)$$

The sea-level density ρ_{SL}, the decay factor β_A (the reciprocal of the scale height), and the mass conversion factor g_0, are adjustable constants. As seen from Table VI (p. 198-199), their nominal values are ρ_{SL} = .002378 slug/ft^3, β_A = 1/24000 ft^{-1}, and g_0 = 32.174 lb/slug.

MVSDP -- Mach Number, Speed of Sound from Air

Density, Pressure.

Inputs: ADENS, air density ρ_A (slug/ft^3);
APRES, air pressure P_A (lb/ft^2).

Outputs: VSND, speed of sound v_s (ft/sec);
EMACH, Mach number M.

Action:

$$v_S = \sqrt{\gamma_A \cdot P_A / \rho_A} \qquad \text{(B-41)}$$

$$M = v_E / v_S \qquad \text{(B-42)}$$

The ratio of specific heats of air, γ_A, is an adjustable constant whose nominal value is, by Table VI, γ_A = 1.4.

<u>TABAA (X, Y, N)</u> -- Aerodynamic Table Interpolation
<u>TABAB (X, Y, N)</u>   Subroutines.

Inputs: X, independent variable for the table.

Outputs: Y, dependent variable interpolated from
table.

Action: Tables of the quantity designated by Y, as
functions of the quantity designated by X,
are assumed to be in table number 5 for
TABAA, and table number 6 for TABAB. A
Lagrangian interpolation of order $N \leq 2$ is
used to find Y from X. If X and Y refer to
ROCKET program variables, a **COMMON** package
must be used when compiling (see Appendix E,
Sec. 5).

<u>TABDPQ</u> -- Tabulated Air Density and Pressure;
Dynamic Pressure.

Inputs: None.

Outputs: ADENS, air density ρ_A (slug/ft^3);
APRES, air pressure P_A (lb/ft^2);
Q, dynamic pressure q (lb/ft^2).

Action: Tables of ρ_A and P_A vs. altitude h_E in feet,
are assumed to be in table number 1. A
second-order Lagrangian interpolation is used
to find ρ_A and P_A from h_E, and Eq. (B-40)
determines q.

TABTVM (NTB, N) -- Tabulated Air Temperature;

Speed of Sound and Mach Number.

Inputs: None.

Outputs: ATEMP, air temperature T_{air} (^{o}R);

VSND, speed of sound v_S (ft/sec);

EMACH, Mach number M.

Action: Tables of T_{air} in degrees Rankine vs. the altitude h_E in feet, are assumed to be in table number NTB. A Lagrangian interpolation of order $N \leq 2$ is used to find T_{air} from h_E; v_S and M are then computed by

$$v_S = \sqrt{\gamma_A \cdot R_G \cdot T_{air}}$$

$$M = v_E/v_S.$$

The ratio γ_A of specific heats of air and the gas constant R_G are adjustable constants whose nominal values are, by Table VI,

$$\gamma_A = 1.4, \quad R_G = 1715 \frac{ft\text{-}lb}{slug\text{-}^{o}R}$$

TALPHA -- Total Angle of Attack and Effective

Roll Angle.

Inputs: ALPHAR, angle of attack α (rad);

BETAR, sideslip angle β (rad).

Outputs: ALPHTD, total angle of attack α_T (deg);

ALPHTR, total angle of attack α_T (rad);

SIGR, effective roll angle σ_R (rad).

Action: Eqs. (B-34) determine α_T and σ_R.

TBCALM (N) -- Tabulated Al-Axis Force Coefficient vs. Mach Number.

Inputs: EMACH, Mach number M;

Q, dynamic pressure q (lb/ft^2);

AREA, reference area of vehicle A_{ref} (ft^2).

Outputs: CAL, Al-axis force coefficient C_{Al};

AAL, aerodynamic force A_{Al} along Al-axis (lb).

Action: A table of C_{Al}, the Al-axis force coefficient, as a function of the Mach number M, is assumed to be in table number 6. A Lagrangian interpolation of order N $\le$ 2 is used to find C_{Al} from M; C_{Al} is then modified by the multiplicative factor C_{AERO}, Eq. (B-33) is then used to find A_{Al}.

TBCAXM (N) -- Tabulated Axial Force Coefficient vs. Mach Number.

Inputs: EMACH, Mach number M;

Q, dynamic pressure q (lb/ft^2);

AREA, reference area of vehicle A_{ref} (ft^2).

Outputs: CA, axial force coefficient C_A;

AAX, aerodynamic force A_A along A-axis (lb).

Action: Tables of C_A vs. M are assumed to be in table
            number 5; C_A is determined from M by a
            Lagrangian interpolation of order $N \leq 2$; it
            is then modified by the multiplicative factor
            C_{AERO}. A_A is obtained by Eq. (B-31).

TBCLAM (N) -- Tabulated C_{A1}/α vs. Mach Number.

Inputs: EMACH, Mach number M;
            ALPHAD, angle of attack α (deg);
            Q, dynamic pressure q (lb/ft^2);
            AREA, reference area of vehicle A_{ref} (ft^2).

Outputs: CAL, A1-axis force coefficient C_{A1};
            AAL, aerodynamic force A_{A1} along A1-axis (lb).

Action: A Lagrangian interpolation of order $N \leq 2$ is
            used to find C_{A1}/α as a function of M, from
            tables assumed to be in table number 6.
            Multiplication by α produces C_{A1}, which is then
            modified by the factor C_{AERO}, and Eq. (B-33)
            is used to find A_{A1}.

TBCNAM (N) -- Tabulated C_N/α_T vs. Mach Number.

Inputs: EMACH, Mach number M;
            ALPHTD, total angle of attack α_T (deg);
            SIGR, effective roll angle σ_R (rad);
            Q, dynamic pressure q (lb/ft^2);
            AREA, reference area of vehicle A_{ref} (ft^2).

Outputs: CN, normal force coefficient C_N;

ABT, aerodynamic force A_B along B-axis (lb);

AAL, aerodynamic force A_{A1} along Al-axis (lb).

Action: A Lagrangian interpolation of order $N \leq 2$ is made to find C_N/α_T from M, using tables assumed to be in table number 6. Multiplication by α_T produces C_N, which is then modified by the factor C_{AERO}. Eq. (B-37) produces A_N, and Eqs. (B-35) then yield A_B and A_{A1}.

TLLDPQ -- Linear Log Air Density and Pressure; Dynamic Pressure.

Inputs: None.

Outputs: ADENS, air density ρ_A (slug/ft^3);

APRES, air pressure P_A (lb/ft^2);

Q, dynamic pressure q (lb/ft^2).

Action: Tables of $\ln(\rho_A)$ and $\ln(P_A)$ vs. altitude h_E in feet, are assumed to be in table number 1. Linear interpolation is used to find $\ln(\rho_A)$ and $\ln(P_A)$ from h_E; their exponentials are taken and q determined by Eq. (B-40).

3. GUIDANCE SUBROUTINES

Planar Approximation for Inertial Angles

If side forces are small during the course of a trajectory, the assumption can be made, without great loss of accuracy, that the velocity vector, vehicle attitude vector, position vector, and initial inertial position vector lie in the same plane. In this case one obtains a simple relation for the inertial attitude angle Θ_I, in terms of the flight path angle γ, the angle of attack α, the vehicle attitude angle Θ, and the inertial range angle Δ_I:

$$\Theta = \alpha + \gamma = \Theta_I + \Delta_I. \qquad (B-43)$$

The situation is depicted in Fig. 37. It should be mentioned that the local horizontal is defined as the plane through the vehicle and perpendicular to the radius vector; it is independent of any geodetic anomalies resulting from an aspherical earth.

Subroutines

CⲞNALB (A, BT) -- Constant Angles of Attack.

Inputs: None.

Outputs: ALPHAR, angle of attack α (rad);

BETAR, sideslip angle β (rad).

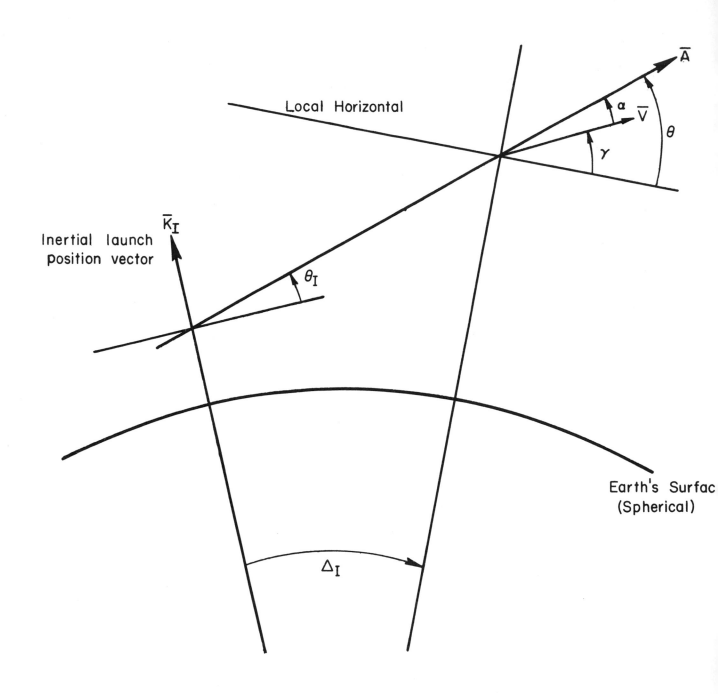

Fig. 37- Inertial Attitude Angle

Action: A and BT are assumed to be α and β, expressed in degrees; they are converted to radians and modified by the multiplicative factor C_{GUID}.

CΦNTHD (TD) -- Constant Attitude Angle Rate $\dot{\Theta}$.

Inputs: None.

Outputs: ALPHAR, angle of attack α (rad);

ALPHAD, angle of attack α (deg);

THETAD, vehicle attitude angle Θ (deg).

Action: TD, after being modified by the multiplicative factor C_{GUID}, is assumed to be $\dot{\Theta}$ in rad/sec. It is placed in location x_1 of the integration block; the current integrated value of Θ is then taken from location x_1, and α is computed by Eq. (B-43). During the first entry to the subroutine, the initial value of Θ, in radians, is computed from initial values of γ and α by Eq. (B-43) and placed in location x_1 of the integration block.

CΦNTHI (TI) -- Constant Inertial Attitude Angle Θ_I.

Inputs: None.

Outputs: THETIR, inertial attitude angle Θ_I (rad);

DELIR, inertial range angle Δ_I (rad);

THETAD, vehicle attitude angle Θ (deg);

ALPHAR, angle of attack α (rad);

ALPHAD, angle of attack α (deg).

Action: TI, after being modified by the multiplicative factor C_{GUID}, is assumed to be Θ_I in degrees and is converted to radians. The subroutine DELI (see Sec. 5 below) is used to find Δ_I. Eq. (B-43) is then employed to find Θ and α.

CØNTHT (TH) -- Constant Attitude Angle Θ.

Inputs: None.

Outputs: THETAD, vehicle attitude angle Θ (deg);

ALPHAR, angle of attack α (rad);

ALPHAD, angle of attack α (deg).

Action: TH, after being modified by the multiplicative factor C_{GUID}, is assumed to be Θ in degrees and is converted to radians. Eq. (B-43) determines α.

CØNTID (TD) -- Constant Inertial Attitude Angle Rate $\dot{\Theta}_I$.

Inputs: None.

Outputs: THETIR, inertial attitude angle Θ_I (rad);

DELIR, inertial range angle Δ_I (rad);

THETAD, vehicle attitude angle Θ (deg);

ALPHAR, angle of attack α (rad);

ALPHAD, angle of attack α (deg).

Action: TD, after being modified by the multiplicative factor C_{GUID}, is assumed to be $\dot{\Theta}_I$ in rad/sec and is placed in location $\dot{x}_1$ of the integration block; the current integrated value of Θ_I is taken from location x_1. Δ_I is then computed by the subroutine DELI (see Sec. 5 below), and Θ and α found through Eq. (B-43). The initial value of Θ_I is calculated and stored in location x_1 of the integration block during the first entry to the subroutine.

QALMAX (QAM, AM) -- Maximum q·α.

Inputs: Q, dynamic pressure q (lb/ft^2).

Outputs: ALPHAR, angle of attack α (rad);

          ALPHAD, angle of attack α (deg).

Action: QAM is assumed to be $(q\alpha)_{max}$, the maximum allowable value of qα, in deg-lb/ft^2. AM is α_{max}, the maximum value of α, in deg. The value of α is the largest one satisfying both constraints:

$$\alpha = \min\left(\frac{(q\alpha)_{max}}{q}, \ \alpha_{max}\right). \qquad (B-44)$$

<u>TABGA (X, Y, N)</u> -- Guidance Table Interpolation
<u>TABGB (X, Y, N)</u>   Subroutines.

Inputs: X, independent variable for the table.

Outputs: Y, dependent variable interpolated from table.

Action: Tables of the quantity designated by Y,
             as functions of the quantity designated by X,
             are assumed to be in table number 3 for
             TABGA and table number 4 for TABGB. A
             Lagrangian interpolation of order $N \leq 2$ is
             used to find Y from X. If X and Y refer to
             ROCKET program variables, a COMMON package
             must be used when compiling (see Appendix E,
             Sec. 5).

<u>TBALTM (N)</u> -- Tabulated Angle of Attack vs. Time.

Inputs: None.

Outputs: ALPHAR, angle of attack α (rad);
             ALPHAD, angle of attack α (deg).

Action: Tables of α in degrees vs. time in seconds
             are assumed to be in table number 3. The
             subroutine TABGA (TIME, ALPHAD, N) is used
             to find α from t; α is modified by the
             multiplicative factor C_{GUID} and then
             converted to radians.

<u>TBBTTM (N)</u> -- Tabulated Sideslip Angle vs. Time.

Inputs: None.

Outputs: BETAR, sideslip angle β (rad).

Action: Tables of β in degrees vs. time in seconds
are assumed to be in table number 4. The
subroutine TABGB (TIME, BETAD, N) is used to
find β from t; β is modified by the
multiplicative factor C_{GUID} and then converted
to radians.

<u>TBTHDT (N)</u> -- Tabulated $\dot{\theta}$ vs. Time.

Inputs: None

Outputs: ALPHAR, angle of attack α (rad);

              ALPHAD, angle of attack α (deg);

              THETAD, vehicle attitude angle θ (rad).

Action: Tables of $\dot{\theta}$ in rad/sec vs. time in seconds
are assumed to be in table number 3. The
subroutine TABGA (TIME, THD, N) is used to
find $\dot{\theta}$ from t. The subsequent action is
the same as that of the subroutine CϕNTHD.

<u>TBTHTM (N)</u> -- Tabulated θ vs. Time.

Inputs: None.

Outputs: THETAD, vehicle attitude angle θ (deg);

              ALPHAR, angle of attack α (rad);

ALPHAD, angle of attack α (deg);

Action: Tables of Θ in degrees vs. time in seconds are assumed to be in table number 3. The subroutine TABGA (TIME, THETAD, N) is used to find Θ from t. Θ is modified by the multiplicative factor C_{GUID} and converted to radians, and Eq. (B-43) is used to find α.

<u>TBTIDT (N)</u> -- Tabulated $\dot{\Theta}_I$ vs. Time.

Inputs: None.

Outputs: THETIR, inertial attitude angle Θ_I (rad);
DELIR, inertial range angle Δ_I (rad);
THETAD, vehicle attitude angle Θ (deg);
ALPHAR, angle of attack α (rad);
ALPHAD, angle of attack α (deg).

Action: Tables of $\dot{\Theta}_I$ in rad/sec vs. time in seconds are assumed to be in table number 3. The subroutine TABGA (TIME, THD, N) is used to find $\dot{\Theta}_I$ from t. The subsequent action is the same as that of the subroutine CØNTID.

<u>TBTITM (N)</u> -- Tabulated Θ_I vs. Time.

Inputs: None.

Outputs: THETIR, inertial attitude angle Θ_I (rad);
DELIR, inertial range angle Δ_I (rad);

THETAD, vehicle attitude angle Θ (deg);

ALPHAR, angle of attack α (rad);

ALPHAD, angle of attack α (deg).

Action: Tables of Θ_I vs. time in seconds are assumed
to be in table number 3. The subroutine
TABGA (TIME, THETID, N) is used to find Θ_I
from t. Θ_I, after being modified by the
multiplicative factor C_{GUID}, is converted to
radians; the subroutine DELI (see Sec. 5
below) finds Δ_I, and Θ and α are determined
by Eq. (B-43).

UPUPUP -- Vertical Rise.

Inputs: None.

Outputs: GAMMAR, flight path angle γ (rad).

Action: Horizontal components of the velocity vector
are arbitrarily set to zero and γ is set to
$\pi/2$.

4. MOMENT SUBROUTINES

Moment Relationships

These subroutines provide a simplified accounting
for the variation of the vehicle's inertial attitude
angle Θ_I due to moments, or torques, about the center of
gravity of the vehicle. The defining relationship is

$$L = I\ddot{\Theta}_I, \qquad (B-45)$$

where L is the resultant moment about the center of gravity, I is the moment of inertia about the center of gravity, and $\ddot{\Theta}_I$ is the second derivative of the inertial attitude angle, which is integrated twice to obtain the inertial attitude angle Θ_I.

As shown in Fig. 38, all moment-producing forces are assumed to act in the pitch plane, formed by the A- and Al-axis of the vehicle, at points located along the longitudinal A-axis. Aerodynamic forces are assumed to act at a point called the center of pressure X_{CP}; thrust forces are assumed to act at a point called the hinge line X_{HL}. The center of gravity X_{CG} of the vehicle also is assumed to lie on the A-axis, and the moment of inertia I is evaluated with respect to rotations about X_{CG} in the pitch plane.

The resultant moment L about the center of gravity is calculated from the formula

$$L = A_{Al} (X_{CG} - X_{CP}) - T_{Al} (X_{HL} - X_{CG}). \qquad (B-46)$$

The value of $\ddot{\Theta}_I$ is placed in location $\dot{x}_2$ of the integration block and integrated to obtain $\dot{\Theta}_I$, which is placed in location $\dot{x}_1$ of the integration block and integrated

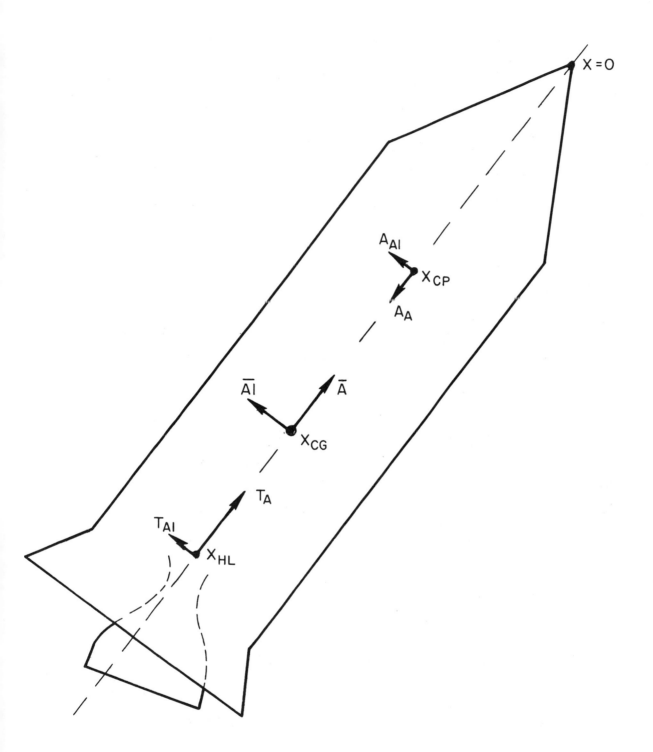

Fig. 38-Moment Calculations

to obtain the attitude angle Θ_I in location x_1. The angle of attack α is then computed from Θ_I, Δ_I, and γ by Eq. (B-43); i.e., $\alpha = \Theta_I + \Delta_I - \gamma$.

The quantities X_{CP}, X_{CG}, and X_{HL} are assumed to be measured in feet, with the value $X = 0$ at the nose of the vehicle, and positive values of X toward the tail of the vehicle.

Subroutines

CØNICG (EMI, CG) -- Constant Moment of Inertia and Center of Gravity.

Inputs: None.

Outputs: ERTIA, moment of inertia I (slug-ft^2);
           XCG, position X_{CG} of center of gravity (ft).

Action: EMI is assumed to be I; CG is assumed to be X_{CG}.

CØNXCP (CP, HL) -- Constant Center of Pressure.

Inputs: None.

Outputs: XCP, position X_{CP} of center of pressure (ft);
           XHL, position X_{HL} of engine hinge line (ft).

Action: CP is assumed to be X_{CP}; HL is assumed to be X_{HL}.

MOMENT -- Vehicle Attitude from Integrated Moments.

Inputs: XCG, position X_{CG} of center of gravity (ft);

XCP, position X_{CP} of center of pressure (ft);

XHL, position X_{HL} of engine hinge line (ft);

ERTIA, moment of inertia I (slug-ft^2);

TAL, thrust force T_{A1} along A1-axis (lb);

AAL, aerodynamic force A_{A1} along A1-axis (lb).

Outputs: THETAD, vehicle attitude angle Θ (deg);

THETIR, vehicle inertial attitude angle Θ_I (rad);

ALPHAR, angle of attack α (rad);

ALPHAD, angle of attack α (deg).

Action: $\ddot{\Theta}_I$ is calculated from Eqs. (B-45) and (B-46)
and placed in location $\dot{x}_2$ of the integration
block. The integrated value $x_2 = \dot{\Theta}_I$ is placed
in location $\dot{x}_1$. The integrated value $x_1 = \Theta_I$
is then used in Eq. (B-43) to compute α. The
initial value of Θ_I is calculated and stored
in location x_1 during the first entry to the
subroutine; x_2 is initially set to zero.

TBCPAL (N, HL) -- Tabulated Center of Pressure vs.
Angle of Attack.

Inputs: ALPHAD, angle of attack α (deg).

Outputs: XCP, position X_{CP} of center of pressure (ft);

XHL, position X_{HL} of engine hinge line (ft).

Action: Tables of X_{CP} in feet vs. α in degrees are assumed to be in table number 3. The subroutine TABGA (ALPHAD, XCP, N) is used to find X_{CP} from α. HL is assumed to be X_{HL}.

TBICGT (N) -- Tabulated Moment of Inertia and Center of Gravity vs. Time.

Inputs: None.

Outputs: ERTIA, moment of inertia I (slug-ft^2); XCG, position X_{CG} of center of gravity (ft).

Action: Tables of X_{CG} and I vs. time in seconds are assumed to be in table number 10. A Lagrangian interpolation of order $N \leq 2$ is used to find X_{CG} and I as functions of t.

TBICGW (N) -- Tabulated Moment of Inertia and Center of Gravity vs. Weight.

Inputs: None.

Outputs: ERTIA, moment of inertia I (slug-ft^2); XCG, position X_{CG} of center of gravity (ft).

Action: Tables of X_{CG} and I vs. weight in lb are assumed to be in table number 10. A Lagrangian interpolation of order $N \leq 2$ is used to find X_{CG} and I as functions of weight.

5. MISCELLANEOUS COMPUTATIONAL SUBROUTINES

CΦAST -- No Nongravitational Forces.

Inputs: None.

Outputs: All orientation angles and nongravitational forces are set to zero.

DELE -- Earth-Referenced Range Angle.

Inputs: None.

Outputs: RXYZG (1), (2), (3), the components of the vehicle position vector $\overline{r}$ in an earth-referenced (x_G, y_G, z_G) system (ft);

DELER, earth-referenced range angle Δ_E (rad).

Action: The position vector $\overline{r}$ in an earth-referenced (x_G, y_G, z_G) coordinate system is given by

$$r_{x_G} = r \cos \phi \cos \lambda$$

$$r_{y_G} = r \cos \phi \sin \lambda \qquad \text{(B-47)}$$

$$r_{z_G} = r \sin \phi.$$

The geometry is shown in Fig. 39. The angle Δ_E is then given by

$$\cos \Delta_E = \frac{\overline{r} \cdot \overline{K}}{|\overline{r}| \cdot |K|} \qquad \text{(B-48)}$$

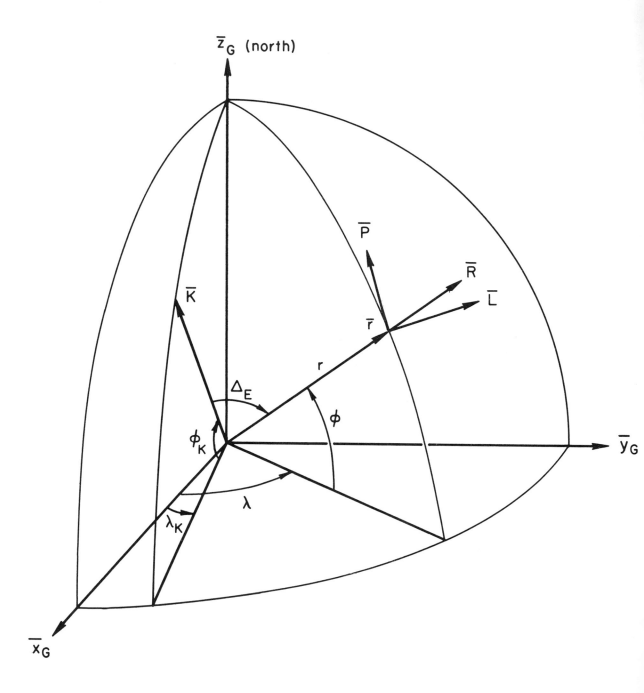

Fig. 39—Earth-Referenced Coordinates

where $\bar{K}$ is the initial (launch) position
vector.

DELI -- Inertial Range Angle.

Inputs: None.

Outputs: XYZI (1), (2), (3), the components of the
            vehicle position vector in an inertial
            (x_I, y_I, z_I) system (ft);
            DELIR, inertial range angle Δ_I (rad).

Action: The inertial (x_I, y_I, z_I) components of $\bar{r}$ are
            computed from Eqs. (3-5); the geometry is
            that of Fig. 10. The angle Δ_I is obtained
            from

$$\cos \Delta_I = \frac{\bar{r} \cdot \bar{K}_I}{|\bar{r}| \cdot |\bar{K}_I|} \qquad (B-49)$$

where $\bar{K}_I$ is the initial inertial position
vector.

EXTRAP -- Vacuum Ballistic Extrapolation.

Inputs: None.

Outputs: VI, inertial velocity v_I (ft/sec);
            GAMID, inertial flight path angle γ_I (deg);
            EGY, energy per unit mass (ft^2/sec^2);
            AFT, semimajor axis a of osculating orbit (ft);

ECC, eccentricity e of osculating orbit;

HAPØG, apogee altitude h_A of osculating orbit (n mi);

RIMP, surface range R_{IMP} between launch point and extrapolated impact point (n mi).

Action: This subroutine computes a number of parameters related to the osculating two-body orbit resulting from a vacuum ballistic extrapolation of the vehicle's current position and velocity. The following formulas are used (see Fig. 40):

$$v_{LI} = r(\dot{\lambda}+\omega) \cos \phi$$

$$v_I = \sqrt{v_R^2 + v_{LI}^2 + v_P^2}$$

$$\gamma_I = \sin^{-1} \frac{v_R}{v_I}$$

$$EGY = \frac{v_I^2}{2} - \frac{\mu}{r} . \qquad (B-50)$$

If EGY = 0, the osculating orbit is a parabola; e is set to unity, and a, h_A, and R_{IMP} are set to zero. If not,

$$r\dot{r} = r \, v_I \sin \gamma_I$$

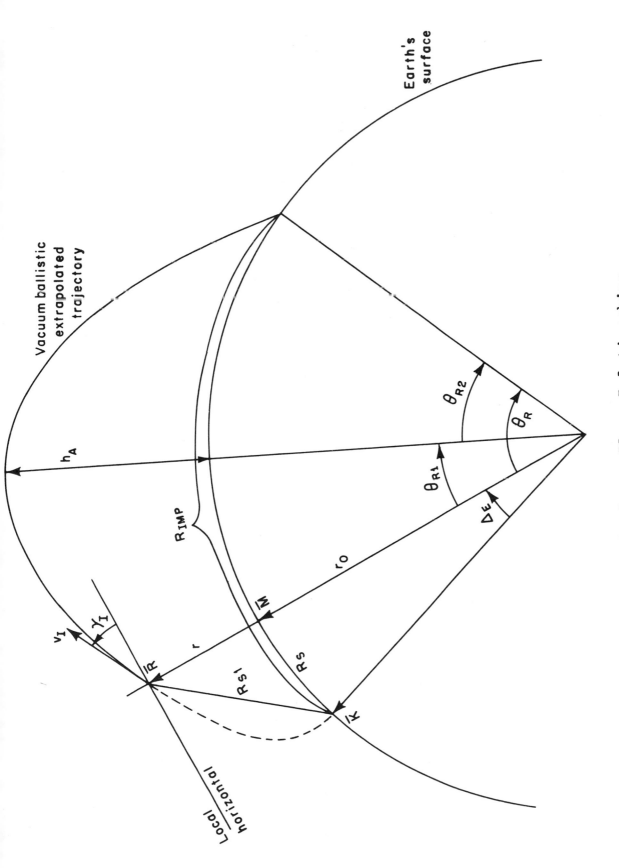

Fig. 40— Range Plane Relationships

$$P = \frac{r^2 v_I^2 - (r\dot{r})^2}{\mu}$$

$$a = \frac{-\mu}{2 \cdot EGY}$$

$$e = \sqrt{1 - \frac{P}{a}}$$

$$h_A = a(1+e) - r_o$$

$$\Theta_{R1} = \cos^{-1}\left(\frac{r-P}{re}\right)$$

$$\Theta_{R2} = \cos^{-1}\left(\frac{r_o - P}{r_o e}\right)$$

$$R_{IMP} = R_S + r_o(\Theta_{R1} + \Theta_{R2}). \qquad (B-51)$$

RANGES -- Surface Range and Slant Range

Inputs: None

Outputs: RANGE, surface range R_S (n mi);

           RWS, slant range R_{Sl} (ft).

Action: Calculation of the surface range R_S is carried

           out in two different ways, depending on

           whether a spherical or oblate earth model is

           being used. The methods used are described

           in Appendix D. The slant range R_{Sl} is

           calculated by the formula (see Fig. 40):

$$R_{S1} = \left[(r_{x_G} - K_{x_G})^2 + (r_{y_G} - K_{y_G})^2 + (r_{z_G} - K_{z_G})^2 \right]^{\frac{1}{2}} .$$

The components $(r_{x_G}, r_{y_G}, r_{z_G})$ of the vehicle position vector in earth-referenced coordinates are calculated by the subroutine DELE; the quantities $(K_{x_G}, K_{y_G}, K_{z_G})$ are the corresponding components of the launch position vector.

REIMP -- Rotating Earth Impact Extrapolations.

Inputs: Must be preceded by the subroutine EXTRAP.

Outputs: RIMP, surface range R_{IMP} between launch point and extrapolated impact point (n mi);

TIMP, time t_H at extrapolated impact (sec);

GIMP, inertial flight path angle γ_H at extrapolated impact (deg);

PHHD, latitude ϕ_H at extrapolated impact (deg);

ELHD, longitude λ_H at extrapolated impact (deg).

Action: This subroutine determines the point of intersection of the vacuum ballistic trajectory determined by the vehicle's current position and velocity with the surface of a rotating spherical earth, plus some parameters associated with this extrapolated impact point.

The angular distance $\Theta_R = \Theta_{R1} + \Theta_{R2}$ between the vehicle and its extrapolated impact point

is calculated by the subroutine EXTRAP. The
normal $\overline{N}$ to the plane of motion, the inclination
i of the plane of motion to the equator, the inertial longitude Ω of the intersection of the plane
of motion with the equator, and the angular position u of the vehicle in the plane of motion, are
obtained by formulas (5-20) through (5-23) on
p. 122. The angular position u_H of the impact
point is

$$u_H = u + \theta_R \; ;$$

the latitude ϕ_H and inertial longitude λ_H of the
impact point are then calculated from the following formulas:

$$x_H = \cos \Omega \cos u_H - \sin \Omega \sin u_H \cos i$$

$$y_H = \sin \Omega \cos u_H + \cos \Omega \sin u_H \cos i$$

$$z_H = \sin u_H \sin i \qquad\qquad (B-52)$$

$$\phi_H = \sin^{-1} z_I$$

$$\lambda_H = \tan^{-1} (y_I/x_I) - \lambda_{G_o} - \omega t \; .$$

To calculate the flight time, we introduce the
quantity

$$\rho = \frac{r \, v_I^2}{\mu}$$

and obtain t_F by the relation: [3]

$$t_F = \frac{r}{v_I \cos \gamma_I} \left[\frac{(1-\cos \Theta_R) \tan \gamma_I + (1-\rho) \sin \Theta_R}{(2-\rho)\left(\frac{r}{r_0}\right)} + \frac{2 \cos \gamma_I}{\rho\left(\frac{2}{\rho} - 1\right)^{3/2}} \tan^{-1}\left(\frac{\sqrt{\frac{2}{\rho} - 1}}{\cos \gamma_I \cot \frac{\Theta_R}{2} - \sin \gamma_I} \right) \right] .$$

$$(B-53)$$

The impact time t_H is determined from the current time t by

$$t_H = t + t_F .$$

The flight path angle γ_H at impact is obtained [3] from

$$\gamma_H = \tan^{-1}\left(\frac{-\left[2 \left(\frac{r}{r_0} - 1\right) + \rho \left(1 - \left(\frac{r}{r_0}\right)^2 \cos^2 \gamma_I\right)\right]^{\frac{1}{2}}}{\frac{r}{r_0} \cos \gamma_I \sqrt{\rho}} \right) .$$

$$(B-54)$$

If the rotating earth model has been specified, the impact longitude, and consequently the surface range, must be revised to account for the motion of the earth during the vehicle's flight. In this case we must replace λ_H by $\lambda_H - \omega\, t_F$, obtain $\bar{r}_H$ in the (x_G, y_G, z_G) system by

$$r_{Hx} = r \cos \phi_H \cos \lambda_H$$

$$r_{Hy} = r \cos \phi_H \sin \lambda_H \qquad \text{(B-55)}$$

$$r_{Hz} = r \sin \phi_H \; ,$$

and compute the range angle Δ_H and the impact range R_{IMP} from the launch position vector $\bar{K}$ by

$$\cos \Delta_H = \frac{\bar{r}_H \cdot \bar{K}}{|\bar{r}_H| \cdot |\bar{K}|} \qquad \text{(B-56)}$$

$$R_{IMP} = r_E \, \Delta_H \; . \qquad \text{(B-57)}$$

This subroutine is used automatically to calculate R_{IMP} if orbital output is called for with the rotating earth model.

VLΦSS -- Velocity Losses Due to Gravity and Drag.

Inputs: ALPHAR, flight path angle (rad);

BETAR, sideslip angle β (rad).

Outputs: DVGR, velocity loss Δv_G due to gravity (ft/sec);

DVDR, velocity loss Δv_D due to drag (ft/sec).

Action: The quantities Δv_G and Δv_D are obtained by
integration, using the formulas (5-13) and
(5-14). Locations $\dot{x}_4$ and x_4 of the integration block are used to integrate Δv_G; locations
$\dot{x}_5$ and x_5 for Δv_D.

6. MACRO-SUBROUTINES

A number of the more commonly used flight programs
have been placed in the ROCKET library as macro-subroutines.
Instead of writing the sequence of references in the
flight program over and over, the user need only write
one reference to the entire program. For example, here
is the macro-subroutine for a common vertical liftoff
flight program:

```
SUBR$\Phi$UTINE UPUP1
CALL UPUPUP
CALL TABDPQ
CALL MVSDP
CALL TBCAXM (2)
CALL TBTFHE (2)
```

```
                  RETURN

                  END
```

Any time a user wants to employ this flight program in a section, he writes CALL UPUP1 and everything is taken care of. He must still supply the tables required by the component subroutines, of course.

Other macro-subroutines that are available are the following:

```
          SUBRØUTINE UPUP2 (CAX, TH, FL, AE)

          CALL UPUPUP

          CALL TABDPQ

          CALL CØNCAX (CAX)

          CALL CTHAIR (TH, FL, AE)

          RETURN

          END


          SUBRØUTINE UPUP3 (N, TH, FL, AE)

          CALL TABDPQ

          CALL MVSDP

          CALL TBCAXM (N)

          CALL CTHAIR (TH, FL, AE)

          CALL UPUPUP

          RETURN

          END
```

```
SUBROUTINE UPUP4 (N, TH, SPI, AE)
CALL TABDPQ
CALL MVSDP
CALL TBCAXM (N)
CALL CTAISP (TH, SPI, AE)
CALL UPUPUP
RETURN
END


SUBROUTINE GTURN1
CALL CONALB  (0.,0.)
CALL TABDPQ
CALL MVSDP
CALL TBCAXM (2)
CALL TBTFHE (2)
RETURN
END


SUBROUTINE  GTURN2 (CAX, TH, FL, AE)
CALL CONALB (0.,0.)
CALL TABDPQ
CALL CONCAX (CAX)
CALL CTHAIR (TH, FL, AE)
RETURN
END
```

```
      SUBROUTINE GTURN3 (N, TH, FL, AE)

      CALL TABDPQ

      CALL MVSDP

      CALL TBCAXM (N)

      CALL CTHAIR (TH, FL, AE)

      RETURN

      END



      SUBROUTINE CTHI1 (CAX, CLA, TH, FL, AE)

      CALL CONTID  (O.)

      CALL TABDPQ

      CALL CONCAX (CAX)

      CALL CONCLA (CLA)

      CALL CTHAIR (TH, FL, AE)

      RETURN

      END



      SUBROUTINE CTHI2 (TH, FL)

      CALL CONTID (O.)

      CALL CONTFL (TH, FL)

      RETURN

      END
```

```
SUBROUTINE CTHI3 (TI, TH, FL)
CALL CONTHI (TI)
CALL CONTFL (TH, FL)
RETURN
END
```

Appendix C
TABLES

Tables can be employed by the user to approximate very complicated or even discontinuous mathematical functions whose use may be necessary to describe the environment of a rocket in flight. A user who has such a function of one or two variables, such as the rocket's thrust as a function of altitude, or the vehicle's normal aerodynamic force coefficient as a function of Mach number and angle of attack, need only tabulate the function once on special input forms; the resulting keypunched cards are placed directly behind the first "0000" card punched from the Flight Control Form (see Table I, p. 22).

Table V (p. 189) is a "table table" which gives the basic layout of the tables in the program. The "table number" is the number by which tables are identified by the computational subroutines (see Appendix B); each computational subroutine employing tables assumes that the tables it uses have a particular table number. This table number is the one entered in the "2995" entry on the table input forms (Figures 3, 4).

The "table type" tells what kinds of tables are identified with a table number; N_1 is the maximum number of entries in the table for the first independent variable; N_2 is the maximum number of entries in the table for the second independent variable. The "base location" tells where in the ROCKET storage block the table is located, and N_{DV} represents the number of dependent variables appearing as functions of the independent variable(s) in the table. The "number of stages" is the number of different tables which can be identified with the same table number and used by the same computational subroutines; more will be said about this feature below.

Figures 3 and 4 (pp. 15, 16) show the standard input forms for one- and two-dimensional tables. The number format for the tables is an eight-digit floating point representation; it is a standard one for all ROCKET inputs and is described in Appendix E, Sec. 4.

The "table number," the first entry on the input form, provides the program with the information it needs to set up the tables properly. This table number must be the same number as the one which the computational sub-routine employing the table assumes is being used. For example, if a flight program uses the subroutine TBTFHE, which assumes that tables of thrust and fuel flow vs. altitude have been placed in table number 2, and the number 3 is entered in the "table number" slot on the table input form when making up the thrust tables, ROCKET will dis-continue the run the first time it calls on the subroutine TBTFHE, and will print the message: "...RUN TERMINATED -- NO THRUST TABLE."

More than one tabular function may be used by a single

computational subroutine during the course of a trajectory.
This sort of situation is handled by means of the next
entry on the input form, the "stage number." From Table
V it can be seen that table number 2 has four stages; i.e.,
four different tables which can act as table number 2.
Thus, when dealing with the two different thrust curves,
one may be assigned a stage number of 1, and the other a
stage number of 2; thus both are loaded into different
parts of table number 2. During the course of the trajectory, then, the table to be used throughout a section
may be specified by placing a 1 or 2 in the "thrust tables"
slot in the Section Conditions for that particular section
on the Flight Control Form (entry --30, explained in Appendix A, Sec. 2). The nominal value for the stage number
is 1; if the slot is left blank, the value 1 will be used.
An example of the use of stage numbers is given in Chap. 4,
Sec. C.

The "number of entries" refers to the number of
entries of the independent variable in the table. On the
two-dimensional table input form there are places for the
number of entries in both independent variables. These
numbers must be less than or equal to the maximum number
of entries for the table as given by Table V.

The next line on the input form is used only if a
blank or zero is in the "table number" position. It is
then used to create a table with the specified base

Table V.

TABLE TABLE

Table Number	Table Type	N_1	N_2	Base Location	N_{DV}	No. of Stages
1	Air Pressure, Density	199		3000	2	1
2	Thrust, Fuel Flow	49		3600	2	4
3	Guidance	49		4200	1	4
4	Guidance	49		4600	1	4
5	Axial Aerodynamics	49		5000	1	4
6	Normal Aerodynamics	49		5600	1	4
7	Arbitrary	49		6200	1	4
8	Arbitrary	49		6600	1	2
9	Arbitrary	49		6800	1	2
10	Arbitrary	49		7000	2	2
11	Arbitrary	49		7300	1	1
12	Arbitrary	99		7400	1	1
13	Arbitrary	99		7600	1	1
14	Arbitrary	99		7800	1	1
15	Arbitrary	199		8000	1	1
16	Axial Aerodynamics	25	10	5000	1	2
17	Normal Aerodynamics	25	10	5600	1	2
18	Arbitrary	25	10	8400	1	2
19	Arbitrary	25	10	9000	1	2
20	Arbitrary	35	10	9600	1	1

location, number of dependent variables N_{DV}, and cycle numbers N_1 and N_2. Tables created in this manner must stay between the locations 3000 and 10000 in the ROCKET storage block; care must be taken that they do not over-run other table areas being used, and that the computational subroutine employing them knows where they are. Also, in creating two-dimensional tables, one must have $N_2 \leq N_1$.

The next line on the form is reserved for a line of comments and identifying remarks about the table; this line will be on the first page of the printed output from the program. The succeeding lines on the form are for the actual numbers comprising the table. Only those lines containing table entries should be keypunched.

Each dependent variable subtable in the two-dimensional table is associated with the corresponding value of the second independent variable in the second independent variable table. For example, in Fig. 4 the numbers in the "Dependent Variable 3" subtable represent a curve of C_N (the dependent variable) vs. Mach number (the first independent variable) for $\alpha_T = 2$ degrees (the third value of the second independent variable α_T).

In all tables the values of the independent variables must be entered in ascending order.

Appendix D
ENVIRONMENTAL MODELS

1. EARTH OBLATENESS

The Flight Control Form has a location (0002) called
OBLAT for specifying the type of earth model to be used
throughout the trajectory. If OBLAT is zero, a spherical
earth is assumed; if not, an oblate ellipsoidal earth is
assumed.

The oblate ellipsoidal earth model assumes that a
meridional section, or "great circle" through the poles,
will take the form of an ellipse with major axis a_E,
minor axis b_E, eccentricity e_E, and flattening f_E (see
Fig. 41). These are related by the following formulas:

$$f_E = \frac{a_E - b_E}{a_E}$$

$$e_E^2 = \frac{a_E^2 - b_E^2}{a_E^2} = f_E \left(2 - f_E\right) \quad . \qquad \text{(D-58)}$$

Altitude Calculations

The relations between the geocentric latitude ϕ
(defined as the angle the vehicle position vector $\bar{r}$ makes
with the equatorial plane), and the geodetic latitude ϕ_{GD}
(defined as the angle made with the equatorial plane by the
normal to the earth's surface), the radial distance r from
the center of the earth, and the altitude h_E above the

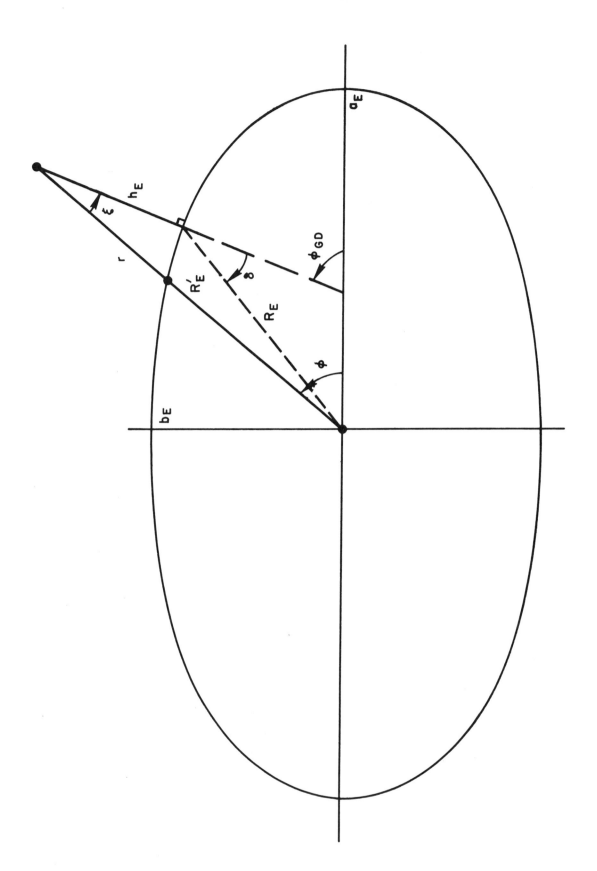

Fig. 41—Meridional Section of Oblate Earth Model

earth's surface, are those in Ref. [4], extended to eight-digit accuracy.

Given h_E, ϕ_{GD}, find r, ϕ:

$$\delta = \frac{e_E^2 \sin \phi_{GD} \cos \phi_{GD}}{1 - e_E^2 \sin^2 \phi_{GD}}$$

$$R_E = b_E \left[1 + \frac{1}{2} e_E^2 \cos^2 \phi_{GD} + \frac{3}{8} e_E^4 \cos^4 \phi_{GD} + \frac{5}{16} e_E^6 \cos^6 \phi_{GD} \right]$$

$$\xi = \frac{R_E \delta}{R_E + h_E}$$

$$r = R_E + h_E \left(1 - \frac{1}{2} \delta \xi \right)$$

$$\phi = \phi_{GD} - \xi. \qquad (D\text{-}59)$$

Given r, ϕ, find h_E, ϕ_{GD}:

$$\delta' = \frac{e_E^2 \sin \phi \cos \phi}{1 - e_E^2 \cos^2 \phi}$$

$$R_E' = b_E \left[1 + \frac{1}{2} e_E^2 \cos^2 \phi + \frac{3}{8} e_E^4 \cos^4 \phi + \frac{5}{16} e_E^6 \cos^6 \phi \right]$$

$$\xi = \frac{R_E \delta'}{r}$$

$$h_E = (r - r_E') \left(1 - \frac{1}{2} \delta' \xi\right)$$

$$\phi_{GD} = \phi + \xi. \tag{D-60}$$

Range Calculations

The surface distance between two points K and M on the ellipsoidal earth is calculated by using the fact that the intersection of the earth's surface with the plane formed by K, M, and the earth's center O will form an ellipse (see Fig. 42).

The inclination i_P of the KMO plane to the equator is determined by expressing K, the launch point, and M, the vehicle's subsurface point, as vectors $\overline{K}$ and $\overline{M}$ in an earth-referenced (x_G, y_G, z_G) system, using the subroutine DELE (see Appendix B, Sec. 5 and Fig. 39, 40), then computing the unit vector $\overline{N}$ normal to the KMO plane as

$$\overline{N} = \frac{\overline{K} \times \overline{M}}{|\overline{K} \times \overline{M}|}, \tag{D-61}$$

and finding i_P from the relation

$$\cos i_P = N_{z_G}. \tag{D-62}$$

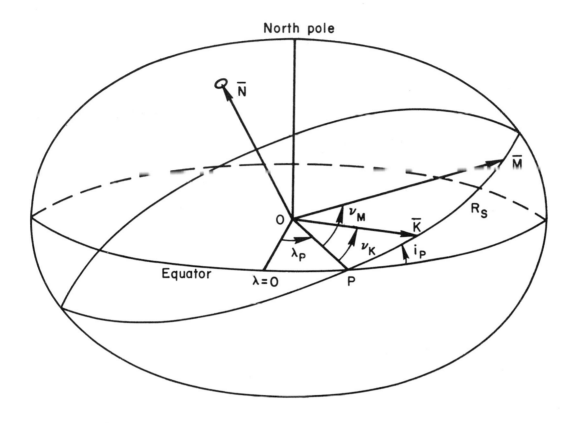

Fig. 42-Oblate Earth Range Computation

The longitude λ_P of the intersection P of the LMO plane with the equator is given by

$$\tan \lambda_P = \frac{N_{x_G}}{-N_{y_G}} \, . \qquad \text{(D-63)}$$

The following formulas then serve to determine the eccentricity e_I of the inclined ellipse, the central angles ν_K and ν_M made by K and M with the equatorial intersection point P, and the surface range R_S:

$$e_I = \frac{e_E \sin i_P}{1 - e_E^2 \cos^2 i_P}$$

$$\sin \nu_{K,M} = \frac{\sin \phi_{K,M}}{\sin i_P}$$

$$\text{(D-64)}$$

$$\cos \nu_{K,M} = \cos \phi_{K,M} \cos (\lambda_{K,M} - \lambda_P)$$

$$R_S = a_E(1 - \frac{e_I^2}{4}) \, (\nu_M - \nu_K) + \frac{a_E e_I^2}{8} \, (\sin 2\nu_M - \sin 2\nu_K).$$

The surface range R_S over a spherical earth is simply $R_S = r_E \cdot \Delta_E$, where r_E is the constant radius of the earth and Δ_E is the earth-referenced range angle, computed by the subroutine DELE.

Gravity Calculations

The gravitational acceleration for a spherical earth acts negatively along the R-axis (see Fig. 10, p. 43); its magnitude is

$$G_R = - \mu/r^2. \qquad (D-65)$$

The gravitational acceleration for an oblate spheroid has two components; one along the R-axis, one along the P-axis; their magnitudes are:

$$G_R = \frac{-\mu}{r^2} \ [1 + \frac{J_E a_E^2}{r^2} (1 - 3 \sin^2 \phi) \ ]$$

$$\qquad (D-66)$$

$$G_P = \frac{-\mu}{r^2} \cdot \frac{J_E a_E^2 \sin 2\phi}{r^2} \ .$$

ROCKET presently uses only the second harmonic component J_E of the oblate earth gravitational potential; higher harmonics may be added in a fairly straightforward fashion if desired.

Program Constants

A list of the constants used by the program and

Table VI

PROGRAM CONSTANTS

Location	Constant	Value	Remarks
2500	r_o	20902287. ft	Average radius of the earth
2501	r_o	3440.0811 n mi	$r_o = (a_E^2 b_E)^{1/3}$
2502	a_E	20925696. ft	Equatorial radius of the earth
2503	f_E	$3.3523299 \cdot 10^{-3}$	Flattening = 1/298.30
2504	e_E	$8.1813334 \cdot 10^{-2}$	Eccentricity
2505	b_E	20855546. ft	Polar radius of the earth
2510	μ	$1.40764548 \cdot 10^{16} \dfrac{ft^3}{sec^2}$	Central force constant GM, earth
2511	J_E	$1.62345 \cdot 10^{-3}$	Second harmonic component of earth gravitational potential
2515	g_o	$32.174 \ ft/sec^2$	Mass conversion factor
2520	w_E	$7.29211585 \cdot 10^{-5} \dfrac{rad}{sec}$	Earth rotation rate (sidereal)
2521	ρ_{SL}	$2.378 \cdot 10^{-3} \ slug/ft^3$	Sea-level atmospheric density

Table VI -- (Continued)

Location	Constant	Value	Remarks
2522	P_{SL}	2116.224 lb/ft^2	Sea-level atmospheric pressure
2523	β_A	1/24000 ft^{-1}	Atmospheric density decay factor
2524	γ_A	1.4	Ratio of specific heats of air
2525	R_G	1715. $\frac{ft-lb}{slug-°R}$	Gas constant
2530	Δt_o	0.25 sec	Initial integration stepsize
2531	$\overline{E}$	.00001	Maximum relative truncation error for integration
2532	A_3	100.	Ratio, maximum to minimum truncation error
2533	A_4	.001	Reference number, relative error computation
2534	Δt_{max}	150. sec	Maximum integration stepsize
2535	Δt_{min}	.01 sec	Minimum integration stepsize
2536	A_1	0.	Integration option flag (see Ref. [5])

their nominal values is given in Table VI above. The geodetic constants are basically those of the DOD World Geodetic System 1960. The location number of each constant is given to enable the user to insert alternate values by means of the input form. For example, if one wished to run a trajectory using the value .00164 for J_E, the number 2511 would be placed in columns 1-4 of one of the Extra Inputs lines on the Flight Control Form (Fig. 1) and the number +164   -02 in columns 6-17.

As another example, if one wished to run the program in "reverse gear" (backwards in time), he would simply place the number 2530 in columns 1-4 of one of the Extra Inputs lines, and the number -25   +00 in columns 6-17.

2. SOLAR-LUNAR EFFECTS

In this simplified formulation, the sun and the moon are assumed to travel in circles with respect to the center of the earth (see Fig. 43). Their position in the earth-centered (x_I, y_I, z_I) coordinate system is given in terms of five orbit parameters:

$i_{s,m}$ the inclination of the sun's or moon's orbit to the equator;

$\Omega_{s,m}$ the angular distance of the ascending node of the orbit, measured eastward in

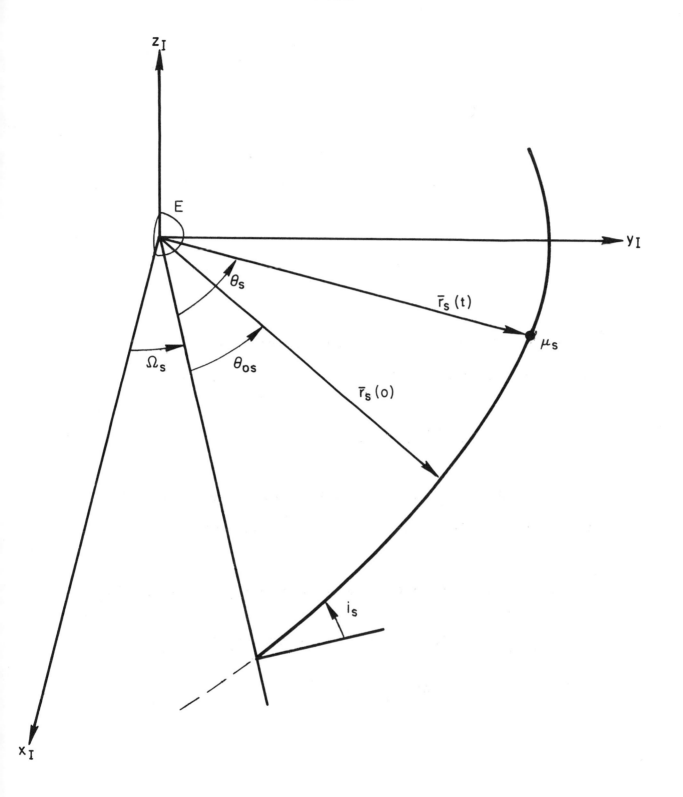

Fig. 43-Circular Solar Orbit

the (x_I, y_I) plane from the x_I-axis, which is nominally pointed toward the vernal equinox;

$(\Theta_o)_{s,m}$ the angular distance of the sun or moon from the ascending node at time $t = 0$;

$w_{s,m}$ the angular rate at which the sun or moon travels along its orbit;

$r_{s,m}$ the radius of the sun's or moon's circular orbit.

At any time t, the position of the sun or moon in its orbit is given by

$$\Theta_s = \Theta_{os} + w_s t . \qquad s \longrightarrow m \qquad (D\text{-}67)$$

The radius vector $\bar{r}_{s,m}$ from the center of the earth to the sun or moon in (x_I, y_I, z_I) coordinates is

$$r_{sx_I} = r_s (\cos \Omega_s \cos \Theta_s - \sin \Omega_s \sin \Theta_s \cos i_s)$$

$$r_{sy_I} = r_s (\sin \Omega_s \cos \Theta_s + \cos \Omega_s \sin \Theta_s \cos i_s)$$

$$r_{sz_I} = r_s (\sin \Theta_s \sin i_s). \qquad s \longrightarrow m$$

$$(D\text{-}68)$$

The effects of the earth's acceleration about the sun and the motion of the earth about the earth-moon barycenter are accounted for by subtracting the accelerations produced by the sun and moon on the earth from those produced by the sun and moon on the vehicle (see Fig. 44). The position $\bar{r}$ of the vehicle in the (x_I, y_I, z_I) system is computed by the subroutine DELI (Appendix B, Sec. 5), and the position $\bar{r}_{vs,m}$ of the sun or moon with respect to the vehicle is obtained by

$$\bar{r}_{vs} = \bar{r}_s - \bar{r} \,. \qquad s \longrightarrow m \qquad (D-69)$$

The acceleration $\Delta\bar{a}_{s,m}$ relative to the earth, produced by the sun or moon on the vehicle is then

$$\Delta\bar{a}_s = \frac{\mu_s \, \bar{r}_{vs}}{|\bar{r}_{vs}|^3} - \frac{\mu_s \, \bar{r}_s}{r_s^{\,3}} \,. \qquad s \longrightarrow m \qquad (D-70)$$

These accelerations are transformed into the (R, L, P) system by

$$(\Delta\bar{a})_{R,L,P} = M_1^{-1}(\lambda_I, \phi) \, (\Delta\bar{a})x_I, y_I, z_I \qquad (D-71)$$

with $M_1(\lambda_I, \phi)$ defined as in Eq. (3-3). They are then added to the other accelerations on the vehicle and integrated by the program.

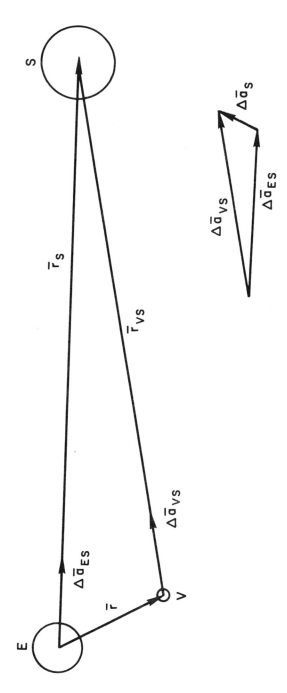

Fig. 44- Solar Acceleration Relative to Earth

Location 0018 of the Initial Conditions on the input form is used to specify the solar-lunar effects:

if = 0, no solar or lunar accelerations are
calculated;

if = 1, lunar accelerations are calculated;

if = 2, solar accelerations are calculated;

if = 3, solar and lunar accelerations are calculated.

The nominal values of the orbit parameters and their location numbers are given below:

LOCATION	PARAMETER	VALUE
2600	μ_s	$4.67898 \cdot 10^{21}$ ft^3/sec^2
2601	r_s	$4.9057972 \cdot 10^{11}$ ft
2602	Ω_s	0. deg
2603	i_s	23.421943 deg
2604	Θ_{os}	0. deg
2605	ω_s	$1.9907247 \cdot 10^{-7}$ rad/sec
2610	μ_m	$1.727 \cdot 10^{14}$ ft^3/sec^2
2611	r_m	$1.2611589 \cdot 10^9$ ft
2612	Ω_m	0. deg
2613	i_m	23.421943 deg
2614	Θ_{om}	0. deg
2615	ω_m	$2.6320458 \cdot 10^{-6}$ rad/sec

Any of these values can be modified by placing the desired number in columns 6-17 of one of the Extra Inputs entries and the corresponding location number in columns 1-4.

Appendix E

OPERATIONAL ASPECTS

1. NUMERICAL INTEGRATION METHODS

Integration Block

Integrations in the ROCKET program take place in an area called the integration block. Derivatives of up to 12 quantities are supplied by the program to the integration block, where they are operated upon by one of two integration routines to produce values of the quantities themselves. The first seven of these twelve quantities are always the state variables h, λ, $\dot{\phi}$, $\dot{h}$, $\dot{\lambda}$, $\dot{\phi}$, and w; the last five are used in certain optional subroutines, but are otherwise available to the user. The program symbols for these five quantities are X1, X2, X3, X4, and X5; the program symbols for their derivatives are X1D, X2D, X3D, X4D, and X5D. The locations X1D and X1 are used by the subroutines CØNTHD, CØNTID, MØMENT, TBTHDT, and TBTIDT; the locations X2D and X2 are used by the subroutine MØMENT; and locations X4D, X4, X5D, and X5 are used by the subroutine VLØSS.

As an example of the use of the integration block, suppose that the effective aerodynamic heating rate of a vehicle as a function of its position and velocity can be calculated, and it is desired to determine the total amount of aerodynamic heating experienced by the vehicle throughout its flight. A subroutine which calculates the heating rate and places it in the location X3D, would then be programmed and included in the flight program for each section of the run; the integrated heat intake would then be available at any point in the location X3. (The locations X1D and X1 could be used just as well, if the flight programs do not refer to any of those above mentioned subroutines which use them.)

Integration Routines

The ROCKET program contains two integration routines, both of which operate in a variable stepsize predictor-corrector mode. The first subroutine is the SHARE subroutine RW INT: Adams-Moulton, Runge-Kutta Integration.[5] It uses the fourth-order predictor and corrector formulas

$$x_{i+1}^{(P)} = x_i + \frac{\Delta t}{24} (55\dot{x}_i - 59\dot{x}_{i-1} + 37\dot{x}_{i-2} - 9\dot{x}_{i-3})$$

$$x_{i+1}^{(C)} = x_i + \frac{\Delta t}{24} (9\dot{x}_{i+1} + 19\dot{x}_i - 5\dot{x}_{i-1} + \dot{x}_{i-2}),$$

obtaining starting values by a fourth-order Runge-Kutta procedure. This subroutine uses double-precision internally to control round-off errors. However, it is

written in FAP, an IBM 704-709-7090 machine-oriented
language, and is thus not available to users of other
machines. ROCKET uses this subroutine to integrate if
the sequence number (location 0001 on the Flight Control
Form) has been entered with a positive sign.

The second subroutine uses the second-order
predictor-corrector formulas due to Southard and Yowell:[6]

$$x^P_{i+1} = 5x_{i-1} - 4x_i + 2 \Delta t (\dot{x}_{i-1} + 2\dot{x}_i)$$

$$x^C_{i+1} = x_i + \frac{\Delta t}{12} (5\dot{x}_{i+1} + 8\dot{x}_i - \dot{x}_{i-1}).$$

This routine is written entirely in FORTRAN source
language; however, it uses only single-precision for
integrations and is not as good at controlling round-off
error as the first routine. It also uses a fourth-order
Runge-Kutta method to obtain starting values, but is
somewhat more efficient at starting or at changing
stepsize, since it requires fewer points to be
recalculated. ROCKET uses this subroutine to integrate
if the sequence number has been entered with a negative
sign on the Flight Control Form.

Variable Stepsize Predictor-Corrector Integration

Here we give a simplified account of the variable
stepsize predictor-corrector method of integration.

Suppose that the vehicle is at the point $\overline{x}_i$ in state space at the time t_i (in Fig. 45 we compress the multidimensional state space of the vehicle, consisting of position, velocity, weight, etc., into a single dimension). We would like to know the vehicle's state vector $\overline{x}_{i+1}$ at the time $t_{i+1} = t_i + \Delta t$.

The flight program computations are able to provide us with the derivative vector $\dot{\overline{x}}_i$ at the time t_i and the point $\overline{x}_i$ (the forces computed are transformed into derivatives by Newton's second law $\overline{F} = m\overline{a}$). But this is the only information we have, besides the past history of $\overline{x}$ and $\dot{x}$; we don't know how these derivatives may be changing as the vehicle goes from $\overline{x}_i$ to $\overline{x}_{i+1}$. So we decide to use the following scheme: We use the derivative $\dot{\overline{x}}_i$, and some of the previous values of $\overline{x}$ and $\dot{\overline{x}}$, to calculate a predicted value $\overline{x}_{i+1}^{P}$ of the state vector at time t_{i+1}. Then we can use $\overline{x}_{i+1}^{P}$ to calculate a predicted value of the derivative vector $\dot{\overline{x}}_{i+1}^{P}$ at the time t_{i+1}. This gives a pretty good idea of how the derivative vector is changing in the interval, and we can then compute an average derivative $\dot{\overline{x}}_{av}$ over the interval and use it to find a corrected value $\overline{x}_{i+1}^{C}$ of the vehicle's state vector at the time t_{i+1}.

If the order of the predictor and the corrector formulas is the same (as is true for the routines used

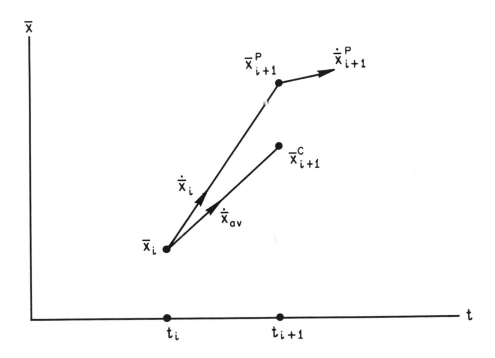

Fig. 45- Predictor-Corrector Integration

in the ROCKET program), we can obtain an estimate of the truncation error $\bar{\epsilon} = |\bar{x}_{i+1} - \bar{x}_{i+1}^{C}|$, where $\bar{x}_{i+1}$ represents the exact solution, as a function of the difference $|\bar{x}_{i+1}^{P} - \bar{x}_{i+1}^{C}|$ between the predicted and corrected values. The magnitude ϵ of this error (which is taken in the ROCKET program to be proportional to the largest component of the adjusted relative error $\dfrac{\bar{\epsilon}}{\max(|\bar{x}_{i+1}^{C}|, A_4)}$), can then be compared with an upper tolerance $\bar{E}$ and a lower tolerance $\bar{E}_1$. If $\epsilon > \bar{E}$, the truncation error is too large, and we cut the stepsize Δt in half and begin again at the point $(t_i, \bar{x}_i)$. If $\epsilon < \bar{E}_1$, we feel we could be sufficiently accurate with a larger stepsize, so we double the stepsize Δt and begin the predictor-corrector process again at $(t_{i+1}, \bar{x}_{i+1}^{C})$. If $\bar{E}_1 \leq \epsilon \leq \bar{E}$, we judge our stepsize to be the correct one, and carry on from $(t_{i+1}, \bar{x}_{i+1}^{C})$ with no modification in Δt.

In the ROCKET program, $\bar{E}$ is an adjustable constant, located in input entry number 2531, with a nominal value of .00001. $\bar{E}_1$ is given as $\bar{E}_1 = \bar{E}/A_3$, where A_3 is in location 2532 with a nominal value of 100. The quantity A_4 is in location 2533 with a nominal value of 0.001. Other quantities regulating Δt are the maximum stepsize Δt_{max} in location 2534 with a nominal value of 150, the minimum stepsize Δt_{min} in location 2535 with a nominal value of 0.01, and the section's print interval Δt_{PO}, which acts as a maximum stepsize.

2. ACCURACY AND SPEED

The tradeoff between accuracy and speed of the ROCKET program is controlled mainly by the adjustable parameter $\bar{E}$, the maximum allowable relative truncation error described in the previous section. The speed of the program when using the nominal value of 10^{-5} for $\bar{E}$ and using the fourth-order integration routine can best be judged by citing the execution times resulting when the four examples of Chap. 4 were run on the IBM 7090.

	Example	Execution Time
1.	Sputsput I	40 sec
2.	Space Taxi	14 min 30 sec
3.	Antigua Venus Probe	3 min 20 sec
4.	Martian Rendezvous	50 sec

The tradeoff between speed and accuracy and the comparison between the two integration methods are shown by the times resulting from variations on the above runs:

	Example	Execution Time
3a.	Antigua Venus Probe, fourth-order, $\bar{E} = 10^{-4}$	2 min 40 sec
3b.	Antigua Venus Probe, fourth-order, $\bar{E} = 10^{-6}$	5 min 30 sec

Example	Execution Time
3c. Antigua Venus Probe, second-order, $\overline{E} = 10^{-5}$	3 min
1c. Sputsput I, second-order, $\overline{E} = 10^{-5}$	1 min

The program generally takes about ten seconds to load on the 7090, plus about ten seconds more if library routines are searched for and read from tape. Compiling k flight programs adds about 10k + 10 seconds extra. Thus, a run with two flight programs to be compiled takes generally about forty seconds to load if library subroutines are included. This number would be reduced to about ten seconds on succeeding runs using the same flight programs, if the flight programs were replaced by the binary cards resulting from the first compilation. Such binary cards should be placed so that they supersede the dummy flight programs in the ROCKET program deck (e.g., in front of the ROCKET deck if the standard IBM FORTRAN loader is being used).

A further comment is given on accuracy in Sec. 8 below.

3. LIST OF GENERAL CAPABILITIES AND LIMITATIONS

The ROCKET program presently handles the following effects:

Aerodynamic forces;

Arbitrary inverse-square force field;

Branching of trajectories;

Earth oblateness effects:

    Ellipsoidal shape;

    Geopotential through second harmonic;

Earth rotation effects, including rotating
    atmosphere;

Iteration on section termination conditions:

    Simple extremalization technique;

Multiple runs;

Multiple section parameter values;

Multiple section termination conditions;

Orbital calculations;

Reverse gear (propagation backwards in time);

Simple guidance schemes;

Simple moment accounting schemes;

Simple propulsion simulations;

Solar-lunar effects;

Tracking calculations.

The program could handle the following effects
with no great strain on its framework:

    Aerodynamic heating calculations;

    Higher harmonics of earth's geopotential;

    Hydrodynamic forces;

    Instantaneous moment balancing;

Multi-section iteration;

Reasonably complicated autopilot simulations;

Reasonably complicated guidance schemes;

Reasonably complicated propulsion simulations;

Simplified structural stress calculations;

Transformations to heliocentric or planetocentric
   coordinate systems;

Winds.

The program was not designed to handle the following
effects:

Detailed bending dynamics and structural stress
   calculations;

Long-term orbital prediction;

Unusually complicated autopilot simulations;

Unusually complicated guidance schemes;

Unusually complicated propulsion simulations.

There is also a mathematical singularity in the
equations of motion at the north and south geographic
poles. A trajectory coming within 0.1 degree of either
pole will be automatically terminated. Generally, this
will happen only for trajectories with initial azimuths
near 0 and 180 degrees.

4. SOME FACTS ABOUT FORTRAN

The user of the ROCKET program will, unless he wishes to program computational subroutines of his own, be concerned with only two things about FORTRAN. One is the characterization of fixed and floating point numbers; the other is the way in which a subroutine is used.

FORTRAN operates with two kinds of numbers, floating point numbers, which are used for all computations in the ROCKET program, and fixed point integers, which are used by the ROCKET program for counting. The following rules always hold true for these two kinds of numbers:

Fixed point constants never contain a decimal point (2,-374);

Floating point constants always contain a decimal point (2.,-.001);

Fixed point variables have names consisting of one to six letters or digits, the first of which is always I, J, K, L, M, or N (I2, KØUNTR);

Floating point variables have names consisting of one to six letters or digits, the first of which is any letter except I, J, K, L, M, or N (A2B2, THRUST).

All FORTRAN statements are written in capital letters. The symbol ф stands for the letter "O"; the symbol O stands for the number zero.

A FORTRAN subroutine is written in the following manner:

SUBROUTINE Name $(a_1, a_2, \ldots, a_n)$

$\Big[$ A number of FORTRAN statements which constitute the subroutine's programmed task; they tell the machine to compute or print desired quantities, or possibly to call on other subroutines to perform their respective programmed tasks. The arguments $a_1, a_2, \ldots, a_n$ appear as dummy variables in this set of statements. $\Big]$

RETURN

END

"Name" refers to the symbolic name of the subroutine, consisting of from one to six letters or digits, the first of which must be a letter and the last of which can be anything but the letter F. There may or may not be any arguments; if there are, they are fixed or floating point variable names. Each statement begins in or to the right of column 7 on a FORTRAN coding form or a ROCKET Flight Programming Form.

A subroutine performs its task when called upon by a CALL statement, which is of the form

CALL Name $(a_1, a_2, \ldots, a_n)$.

This statement transfers control of the machine to the subroutine whose symbolic name is that designated in the "Name" position of the CALL statement, and presents the subroutine with the arguments $a_1, a_2, \ldots, a_n$. These arguments must be fixed point expressions (constants or variables) if the corresponding SUBROUTINE argument

is a fixed point variable; or floating point expressions
(constants or variables) if the corresponding SUBRØUTINE
argument is a floating point variable. If this rule is
not followed, all kinds of horrible things can happen.

When the subroutine completes its programmed task,
its RETURN statement transfers control of the machine
back to the next statement after the CALL statement.

Following are some examples of subroutines.

```
SUBRØUTINE CØNTFL (TH,FL)
THRUST = TH
TAX = TH
WD = -FL
RETURN
END
```

The programmed task of this subroutine is to place the
first argument in the cells containing total thrust
(THRUST) and axial thrust (TAX), and to place the
negative of the second argument in the cell containing
the weight derivative (WD).

```
SUBRØUTINE TBALTM (N)
CALL TABAA (TIME, ALPHAD, N)
ALPHAR = ALPHAD* .0174532925
RETURN
END
```

This subroutine calls on another subroutine, TABAA, which has been programmed to conduct a Lagrangian interpolation of order N to find the angle of attack α in degrees (ALPHAD) from a table of α as a function of time (TIME). It then converts α to radians (ALPHAR).

```
SUBRØUTINE SECT4
CALL CØNTFL (10000., 28.5714)
CALL TBALTM (2)
RETURN
END
```

This subroutine is a ROCKET flight program which calls on the two subroutines given in the examples above. It specifies for its vehicle an axial thrust of 10,000 lb, a weight derivative of -28.5714 lb/sec, and an angle of attack obtained as a tabular function of time by a Lagrangian interpolation of order 2. Note especially that floating point arguments in the called subroutines have floating point constants as corresponding arguments in the CALL statement, and fixed point arguments in the called subroutines have fixed point constants as corresponding arguments in their CALL statement.

Actually, there is a great deal more to FORTRAN, and even to the SUBRØUTINE and CALL statements, than has been sketched here. A complete description of the

FORTRAN language can be found in the literature.[7]

Both input and output to the ROCKET program are in standard formats, each consisting of an eight-digit decimal fraction with the decimal point assumed to be at the left of the first digit, and a two-digit decimal exponent indicating the number of places the decimal point should be shifted to the right to arrive at the desired number. For example, the numbers -0.2, 27347.556, -0.0007451, and 1.0 would be expressed in the following manner on a ROCKET input form:

$-2_{bbbbbbb}+00$, $+27347556+05$, $-7451_{bbbb}-03$,

$+1_{bbbbbbb}+01$,

where the subscripted "b" stands for a blank space. The same numbers would be expressed in the following manner in a ROCKET printout:

-0.20000000E 00, 0.27347556E 05, -0.74510000E-03, 0.09999999E 01.

The only really remarkable thing here is the treatment of the number 1.0. It results from an idiosyncrasy in the (IBM 704-709-7090) FORTRAN program which converts binary machine numbers to decimal output numbers and does not necessarily mean that the number is not exactly 1.0 in the machine. A similar thing happens to a number of other floating point integers.

5. COMPILING AND OPERATING SYSTEM INFORMATION

COMMON Package

Communication between the various ROCKET subroutines is effected by means of the COMMON package shown in Fig. 46, which defines the locations of all program variables in the COMMON area. Any subroutine containing a reference to one or more of these program variables must be compiled with this COMMON package included, in order to insure proper communication. Most flight programs will not need the COMMON package.

Input-Output

Input and output statements in the program are written to work within the IBM SHARE operating system and may require modification to work in other operating systems. All input statements are of the form:

READ INPUT TAPE 5, N, LIST;

and all output statements of the form

WRITE ØUTPUT TAPE 6, N, LIST.

Subroutines Used

SIN, CØS: sine and cosine

LØG, EXP: natural logarithm and

exponential

```
      EQUIVALENCE (B(1),BLOCK(1)),   (H(1),THISEC(1)),  (T(2),TIME)
     A,(T(3),DTIME),(T(4),HFT),   (T(5),ELONR),(T(6),PHIR),  (T(7),HD)
     B,(T(8),ELD),   (T(9),PHD),   (T(10),WGT),  (T(11),X1 ),  (T(12),X2 )
     C,(T(13),X3),   (T(14),X4),   (T(15),X5),   (T(16),HD1),  (T(17),ELD1)
     D,(T(18),PHD1),(T(19),HDD),  (T(20),ELDD),(T(21),PHDD),(T(22),WD)
     E,(T(23),X1D ),(T(24),X2D ),(T(25),X3D), (T(26),X4D),  (T(27),X5D)
      EQUIVALENCE (B(1),INCOND(1)),  (B(100),SECOND(1)),  (B(1),SEQNO)
     A,(B(2),OBLAT),(B(3),ROTAT),(B(4),XINC),  (B(5),TZ),    (B(6),ALTZ)
     B,(B(7),PHIZ),  (B(8),ELONZ),(B(9),VELZ), (B(10),GAMZ),(B(11),PSIVZ)
     C,(B(12),WGTZ),(B(13),PLZ),  (B(14),ELLZ),(B(15),ELGZD),(B(16),ALZD)
     D,(B(17),BTZD),(B(18),ENBODY),(B(19),B18),(B(20),ENTR),(B(21),PT1)
     E,(B(22),ET1),  (B(23),AT1),  (B(24),PT2), (B(25),ET2),  (B(26),AT2)
     F,(B(27),PT3),  (B(28),ET3),  (B(29),AT3)
      EQUIVALENCE (B(2460),COMENT(1)),  (B(2500),RZFT),  (B(2501),RZNM)
     A,(B(2502),AEFT),  (B(2503),FLAT),  (B(2504),EECC),  (B(2505),BE)
     B,(B(2510),EMJ),   (B(2511),EJ),    (B(2512),EH3),   (B(2513),EH4)
     C,(B(2515),GZ),    (B(2520),WER),  (B(2521),SLDENS),(B(2522),SLPRES)
     D,(B(2523),BTAIR),(B(2524),GAMAIR),(B(2525),RGAS),(B(2530),DTZ)
     E,(B(2531),A2),    (B(2532),A3),    (B(2533),A4),    (B(2534),A5)
     F,(B(2535),A6),    (B(2536),A7),    (B(2600),EMUS),  (B(2601),RRS)
     G,(B(2602),OMSD),  (B(2603),QISD),  (B(2604),TQSD),  (B(2605),WWS)
     H,(B(2610),EMUM),  (B(2611),RRM),   (B(2612),OMMD),  (B(2613),QIMD)
     I,(B(2614),TQMD),  (B(2615),WWM)
      EQUIVALENCE (H(1),ELTC),  (H(2),TQ(1)),  (H(6),WJETT),  (H(7),TILT)
     A,(H(8),AREA),  (H(9),CTHR),  (H(10),CFFL),  (H(11),CAERO),(H(12),CGUID)
     B,(H(13),CEXT),(H(14),H13),  (H(15),H14),  (H(16),EMVFL),(H(17),EMV(1))
     C,(H(21),DTPC),   (H(22),OAERO),   (H(23),OTRAC),   (H(24),OORB)
     D,(H(25),OGUID),  (H(26),OSPEC1),  (H(27),OSPEC2),  (H(28),OSPEC3)
     E,(H(29),ALTC),   (H(30),ALTTQ),   (H(31),TTHR),    (H(32),TAERO)
     F,(H(33),TGUID),  (H(34),TEXT),    (H(35),H34)
      EQUIVALENCE (NT(1),NTTHR),(NT(2),NTAERO),(NT(3),NTGUID),
     A    (NT(4),NTEXT),  (HEFT,ALT),  (VELE,VE)
      DIMENSION AMAT(3,3),ARLP(3),B(10000),BLOCK(10000),CAT(3),CET(3)
     A,COMENT(40),DFM(3),DFOB(3),DFS(3),DPFRZ(20,36,2),EIMAT(3,3),EMV(4)
     B,EMAT(3,3),ENNS(3),FABAL(3),FREEZR(20),FRLP(3),H(100),IBAST(20)
     C,IC1T(20),IC2T(5),IDVT(20),INCOND(100),NT(5),REFRG(20),RHO(3)
     D,RT(3),RXYZG(3),RXYZT(3,3),SAT(3),SECOND(100,20),SET(3),T(200)
     E,TAD(3),TED(3),THISEC(100),TMAT(3,3,3),TQ(4),VRLP(3),XYZDI(3)
     F,XYZI(3)
      COMMON AAX,ABT,AAL,ADENS,AEU,AFT,ALPHAD,ALPHAR,ALPHTD,ALPHTR,ALREF
     A,AMAT,APRES,ARLP,AXCEL,B,BETAD,BETAR,BLANKS,BTREF,CA,CAL,CB,CAT
     B,CET,CGAM,CIM,CIS,CLI,CLM,COM,COMS,CPM,CPZ,CPSIV,CYCLE,DELER,DELIR
     C,DFM,DFOB,DFS,DPFRZ,DVDR,DVGR,ECC,EGY,EIMAT,ELGZR,ELHD,ELI,ELZR
     D,EMACH,EMAT,ENNS,ERTIA,FABAL,FLIT,FREEZR,FRLP,FTNM,GAMI,GAMID
     E,GAMMAD,GAMMAR,HALT,HAPI,HAPOG,HEFT,I1,I2,IBAST,IC1T,IC2T,IDVT
     F,IPUT,ISECC,ISECT,ISEQ,  ITAKE,ITC,JPUT,JTAKE,LTC,LTCA,MVF,NEQ,NOP
     G,NT,NTRAC,OMGM,OMGS,OUT1,PASS,PHHD,PHIRGD,PHIZR,PI,PSIVD,PSIVR
     H,PSIVZR,Q,QIM,QIS,RANGE,RCP,RD,REFRG,REFT,REVS,RFT,RHO,RIMP,RPLOP
      COMMON RRD,RT,RWS,RXYZG,RXYZT,RZ,RZI,SAT,SECST,SET,SGAM,SIGR,SIM
     A,SIS,SLI,SLM,SOM,SOS,SPM,SPSIV,SPZ,STOP,T,TAD,TAUAL,TAUBT,TAX,TBT
     B,TAL,TED,THD,THETAD,THETAR,THETIR,THISEC,THM,THRG,THRU,THRUST,THS
     C,THOM,THOS,TIMP,TINT,TMAT,TPLOP,TPO,TQI,VELE,VELH,VI,VRLP,VSND,WE
     D,WFC,XAX,XBT,XAL,XCG,XCP,XHL,XYZDI,XYZI,XZ,YZ,ZZ,XZI,YZI,ZZI,ZERO
     E,ZZZ1,ZZZ2,ZZZ3,ZZZ4,ZZZ5
```

Fig. 46-ROCKET Program COMMON Package

SQRT: square root

ATAN: $\tan^{-1}(x)$

Input and output subroutines

(see above)

Storage Requirements

A storage capacity of at least 32,768 words is required. The distribution of the program in the core storage of the IBM 7090 is approximately as follows (octal notation):

00144 - 22000	Basic ROCKET subroutines;
22000 - 31000	Removable ROCKET computational subroutines;
31000 - 36000	General subroutines described above;
36000 - 50000	Unused;
50000 - 54000	COMMON storage: program variables;
54000 - 72000	COMMON storage: tables;
72000 - 77461	COMMON storage: input.

FAP Subroutines

The ROCKET program is written entirely in FORTRAN source language except for three subroutines written in FAP, an IBM 704-709-7090 machine-oriented language. One of these subroutines is the Adams-Moulton, Runge-Kutta integration routine described in Sec. 1 of this Appendix;

here an alternate integration routine is available for users who cannot process FAP. The other two are small subroutines performing functions not expressible in basic FORTRAN source language; these would have to be rewritten for non-FAP computers.

HELP (X)   This subroutine causes cell X to be filled with BCI blanks.

MZE (X,Y)   This subroutine sets

$$Y = 1., \text{ if } X = -0.;$$

$$Y = 0., \text{ otherwise.}$$

It is needed to differentiate between the read-in of a zero and the read-in of a blank field, which is signified in IBM FORTRAN by -0.

FAP has also been used to supply the FORTRAN loader with dummy entry points for the subroutines SECT1-SECT20, PSPEC1-PSPEC3, and ITER8.

6. COMMON PITFALLS

Here is a checklist of the most common types of errors made in setting up ROCKET runs. It is a good idea to check this list before submitting runs to the computer.

1. The most common errors by far are mechanical errors in input data: mis-keypunched cards, wrong numbers entered on input forms, right numbers entered in the wrong places (e.g., the wrong

section), incorrect number of "0000" cards, tables placed out of order (see Table I, p. 22 for order of input).

2. Improper choice of units for input data.

3. Initial azimuth of 0° or 180° on long flight, sending vehicle over pole (see p. 216).

4. Specifying a termination condition which will never be reached (or which has been reached before the start of the section). Play it safe and use the alternate termination condition to put in some reasonable upper limit on time, altitude, etc.

5. Terminating a section on a condition which isn't being calculated, or which is being calculated only at output points (see p. 59).

6. Omitting calculation of inputs required by flight program subroutines (see p. 59).

7. Exceeding dimension statements: more than 36 branches, more than 20 sections, more table stages or entries in tables than are available, etc.

8. Placing binary flight program decks at wrong end of ROCKET program deck. For the standard IBM FORTRAN loader, the back end is the wrong end, but your installation may differ.

9. On very long runs or runs to determine extremely accurate or very sensitive functions of flight parameters, the nominal truncation error bound of

0.00001 may be too large to ensure significant
results (see p. 212).

10. Irregular spacing of independent variables in
tables involving second-order or parabolic interpolation. Suppose you have a table in which C_A is a
constant 0.4 above Mach 5. If the last three points
in your table are as in the figure below, a parabolic
interpolation will give spurious results.

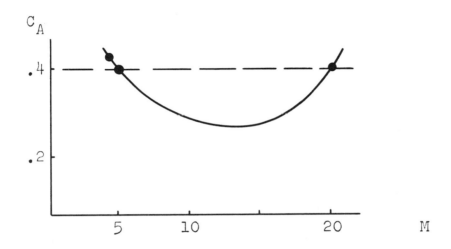

<u>7.</u> <u>SOME INFORMATION FOR THE ADVANCED USER</u>

The computational subroutines presented in this version
of the ROCKET program have been selected mainly for their
simplicity and frequency of use. One reason that more
detailed routines have not been included is that they tend
to become over-specialized; such routines are often easier
to program completely to one's own specifications than to
obtain by modifying a related routine. Another reason is

that a number of detailed routines would easily fill up the remaining core storage without being exhaustive; it has been considered to be more advantageous in the long run to let the user decide how he wishes to use the rest of the core storage.

Thus, the program has been designed to make it easy to incorporate additions and extensions. The flight program structure described in Chap. 3 provides a convenient and well-defined interface between the main program and the computational subroutine; the special output routines described in Chap. 5, Sec. A provide a similar interface for output subroutines.

It has been found that practically all additions to the program can be made within the computational subroutine-flight program framework. When a subroutine is called via the flight program for a section, it is placed in complete control of the machine at each integration point along the trajectory during that section, and presented with the basic trajectory variables (enumerated in Table III, p. 56) and any further quantities computed by preceding subroutines in the flight program. The subroutine may then compute any effects desired; to get these effects to feed back into the trajectory, the subroutine need only resolve them into the quantities specified in Table IV, p. 60. Thus, a particular guidance subroutine, say, must express the effect of its control scheme in terms of the resulting angle of attack α

and sideslip angle β relating the vehicle axes to the coordinate systems based on the vehicle's position and
velocity.

Some of the resources available to the programmer of
ROCKET computational subroutines are the following:

1. Quantities computed by the main program or by
ROCKET computational subroutines called in the flight
program; program symbols and units for these quantities are given in the List of Symbols.

2. Locations B(30) through B(99) for initial condition
inputs.

3. Locations B(135)-B(199),...,B(2035)-B(2099) for
section condition inputs (see p. 135).

4. Locations B(2100)-B(2450) and B(2650)-B(2990) for
other inputs.

5. Locations B(3000)-B(9999), nominally reserved for
tables, are available for other uses as long as these
do not conflict with tables used during the trajectory.

6. About 6000 cells in which to locate new subroutines (assuming a core storage of 32,768 cells).
Another 2500 cells can be obtained by removing all
unused computational subroutines from the program
deck (see Sec. 5 above).

Most additions to the program can thus be made in a
fairly straightforward fashion. As an example, suppose
one wishes to control the inertial attitude angle θ_I of a

vehicle by varying the thrust deflection angle τ_α by means of a second-order differential equation of the form

$$\ddot{\tau}_\alpha = k_1 \dot{\tau}_\alpha + k_2 \tau_\alpha + k_3 \dot{\Theta}_I + k_4 (\Theta_I - \bar{\Theta}_I(t)),$$

where $\bar{\Theta}_I(t)$ is a reference function specified by a table. One way of accomplishing this would be to write a flight program or set of flight programs including, besides references to the appropriate propulsion and aerodynamic subroutines, the following statements:

    CALL THDEDE

    CALL THRESN

    CALL MØMENT

The subroutine MØMENT is described on p. 169 and the subroutines THDEDE (thrust deflection differential equation) and THRESN (thrust resolution) are given below:

```
      SUBRØUTINE THDEDE
      CALL TABGA (TIME, THIBAR, 2)
      THIBAR = THIBAR * RD
      DTHI = X1 - THIBAR
      X4D = B(30) * X4 + B(31) * X3 + B(32) * X2
A         + B(33) * DTHI
      X3D = X4
      RETURN
      END
```

SUBROUTINE THRESN

TAUAL = X3/RD

TAX = THRUST * COSF(X3)

TAL = THRUST * SINF(X3)

RETURN

END

Comments:

The subroutine TABGA (p. 162) obtains $\overline{\Theta}_I$ by parabolic interpolation from a table vs. time which has been placed in table number 3.

RD is a cell containing the number of radians per degree.

The subroutine MOMENT ensures that the vehicle's current inertial attitude angle Θ_I is located in cell X1 (in radians). Since the subroutine MOMENT uses the locations X1 and X2 of the integration block to integrate Θ_I and $\dot{\Theta}_I$, the locations X3 and X4 are used by THDEDE to integrate τ_α and $\dot{\tau}_\alpha$.

The constants k_1-k_4 will be entered via locations 30-33 of the Flight Control Form (entered on one of the Extra Inputs lines). See p. 130.

The integrated value of τ_α is converted to degrees and placed in the cell TAUAL (p. xxvi) so that it can be printed if desired.

The thrust produced by the vehicle's engines is assumed to have been computed and placed in the cell

THRUST by a previous subroutine.

Some extensions may be easier to accomplish by changing the main program rather than operating via the flight program. The larger subroutines in the ROCKET source deck have been annotated fairly liberally with comment cards to give the programmer a clearer picture of what is going on in them. One such extension may be the addition of further cells to the integration block; this can be handled by modifying the COMMON package and the statement NEQ = 12 in the subroutine FARCE and recompiling all subroutines.

8. A NOTE ON PROGRAM RELIABILITY

A number of successful checks have been made on the ROCKET program by means of hand computations, comparisons with respect to analytical solutions of specific trajectory problems, and comparisons with trajectories produced by similar programs. For instance, several perturbation-free orbits were integrated through one revolution with $\overline{E} = 10^{-6}$; the osculating orbital elements printed along the orbit agreed to within five decimal places. Also, the integrated trajectories have displayed a high degree of stability with respect to small changes in initial conditions or flight parameters.

However, there is no guarantee that the program works perfectly all the time. The number of possible configurations that can be set up with the program is extremely large; even after extensive checking and considerable operational experience over the last year and a half, only a small fraction of these configurations has been tried.

We view this somewhat as a blessing in disguise, believing that a slight amount of healthy skepticism is a good thing to have when dealing with a large computer program. If the program is used as an aid to analysis rather than as a substitute for analysis, the user should have no trouble determining whether the program is producing the results desired.

REFERENCES

1. Johnson, S. M., Best Exploration for Maximum is Fibonaccian, The RAND Corporation, RM-1590-PR, November 18, 1955.

2. Schilling, G. F., Limiting Model Atmospheres of Mars, The RAND Corporation, R-402-JPL, August 1962.

3. Wheelon, A. D., "Free Flight of a Ballistic Missile," ARS Journal, Vol. 29, No. 12, December 1959.

4. Purcell, E. W., and W. B. Cowan, "Relating Geodetic Latitude and Altitude to Geocentric Latitude and Radius Vector," ARS Journal, Vol. 31, No. 7, July 1961.

5. Causey, R., and W. L. Frank, Adams-Moulton, Runge-Kutta Integration Subroutine, Space Technology Laboratories, SHARE Distribution Agency, No. 602, November 30, 1958.

6. Southard, T. H., and E. C. Yowell, "An Alternative Predictor-Corrector Process," MTAC, 6, 1952, p. 253.

7. Reference Manual, 709/7090 FORTRAN Programming System, International Business Machines Corporation, Form C28-6054-2, January 1961.

BIBLIOGRAPHY

In this manual it has been unfortunately necessary to present a number of formulas in a somewhat ad hoc fashion, obscuring some of the fascinating physical and mathematical structure which forms the theoretical foundation and environment of the ROCKET program. The theoretical framework for formulas used in the program has been provided in a number of books already available. The list that follows describes those books that the author has found most helpful and stimulating.

Numerical Integration of Differential Equations

Collatz, L., The Numerical Treatment of Differential Equations, Springer-Verlag, Berlin, 1960.

A comprehensive theoretical discussion, but with no lack of illustrative examples; treated with strong insight and characteristic German thoroughness. Also contains excellent coverage of partial differential equations and two-point boundary-value problems.

Hamming, R. W., Numerical Methods for Scientists and Engineers, McGraw-Hill, New York, 1962.

One of the best all-around books on numerical analysis, with an original presentation on methods of developing appropriate integration formulas. The motto of this book, "The purpose of computing is insight, not numbers," is worth a minute's thought for anyone engaged in computational studies.

Henrici, P. K., Discrete Variable Methods in Ordinary Differential Equations, Wiley, New York, 1962.

Contains the best results on error analysis available today, including the author's significant theoretical and experimental results on propagation of round-off error.

Milne, W. E., Numerical Solution of Differential Equations, Wiley, New York, 1953.

A thorough presentation by a pioneer in the field of predictor-corrector integration formulas and methods. Extensive treatment of classical integration formulas.

Rocketry and Flight Mechanics

Davis, L., J. W. Follen, and L. Blitzer, Exterior Ballistics of Rockets, Van Nostrand, Princeton, New Jersey, 1958.

Theoretical and experimental results on the performance of unguided missiles. Excellent mathematical treatment of aerodynamics and rigid body dynamics.

Ehricke, K. A., Space Flight: I. Environment and Celestial Mechanics; II. Dynamics, Van Nostrand, Princeton, New Jersey, 1960, 1962.

A prodigious, monumental work by an outstanding authority and leader in the field of astronautics. Comprehensive treatment of problems ranging over the entire domain of flight dynamics. However, the discussion of trajectory analysis by digital computer is overly simplified and pessimistic.

Koelle, H. H., ed., Handbook of Astronautical Engineering, McGraw-Hill, New York, 1961.

A veritable encyclopedia of astronautics, even including a short discussion of the much-neglected area of cost analysis. The articles, written by outstanding researchers in their fields, are at a consistently high technical level and are quite well coordinated; especially valuable are the extensive bibliographies at the end of each article.

Miele, Flight Mechanics: I. Theory of Flight Paths, Addison-Wesley, Reading, Massachusetts, 1962.

Aircraft and rocket flight mechanics derived from a sound foundation of classical mechanics, containing numerous analytic solutions to specific (though sometimes quite idealized) trajectory problems. The present volume deals mainly with flat-earth trajectories.

Puckett, A. E., and S. Ramo, ed., Guided Missile Engineering, McGraw-Hill, New York, 1959.

A number of articles by specialists in their fields, based on a lecture course given by University of California Extension. Generally good introductions to the major fields comprising guided missile engineering. The treatment of trajectory analysis is rather weak, but the accounts of aerodynamics and design integration are excellent.

Siefert, H. S., ed., Space Technology, Wiley, New York, 1959.

Although based on lectures given five years ago in a University of California extension course, this set of articles by specialists still provides an authoritative and highly readable account of the state of the art in astronautics, at a fairly advanced technical level. Propulsion and flight dynamics are treated especially well; aerodynamics quite sketchily.

<u>Space Trajectories</u>, Academic Press, New York, 1960.

Proceedings of a symposium attended by most of the outstanding men in the trajectory analysis field. Contains much valuable information on practical experience in computing trajectories, although the balance of the book tends more toward orbit analysis--i.e., analysis based on the assumption of a reference orbit--than toward the Cowell-method techniques used in the ROCKET program.

GENERAL INDEX

(General Index)

(General Index)

(General Index)

SUBROUTINES' INDEX

(Where the subroutine has more than one reference,
the key reference pages are underlined.)

(Subroutines' Index)

(Subroutines' Index)

MACRO-SUBROUTINES

FLIGHT CONTROL AND FLIGHT PROGRAMMING FORMS

On the following two pages are reproduced actual, Flight Control and Flight Programming Forms. They can be used for reference while reading the Manual, which refers to them continually. They are also suitable for duplication of copies for use with the program.

ROCKET TRAJECTORY PROGRAM—INPUT FORM

DESCRIPTIVE REMARKS

4 6	10	15	20	25	30	35	40	45	50	55	60	65	
2460													
2470													
2480													
2490													
0000 (A)													

INITIAL CONDITIONS

4 6	15 17 19	28 30 32	41 43 45	54 56 58 67 69
0001	SEQUENCE NO.	OBLAT.	ROTAT.	INCON.
0005	TIME	ALT.	LAT.	LONG. / VEL.
0010	GAMMA	AZIM.	WGT.	LAUNCH LAT. / LAUNCH LONG.
0015	INER. REF. LONG.	ALPHA	BETA	N BODY
0020	NO. TRACKERS	LAT. T1	LONG. T1	ALT. T1 / LAT. T2
0025	LONG. T2	ALT. T2	LAT. T3	LONG. T3 / ALT. T3

SECTION CONDITIONS

	TERMINATION COND.	TERM V1	TERM V2	TERM V3	TERM V4
0100					
0200					
0300					
0400					

	JETT. WGT.	TILT ANGLE	REF. AREA	THRUST COEF	F.F. COEF.
0105					
0205					
0305					
0405					

	AERO. COEF.	GUID. COEF.	EX. COEF.		
0110					
0210					
0310					
0410					

	MULT. VAL. FLAG.	V1	V2	V3	V4
0115					
0215					
0315					
0415					

	PRINT INTERVAL	AERO. P.O.	TRACKER P.O.	ORBIT P.O.	GUID. P.O.
0120					
0220					
0320					
0420					

	SPEC. P.O.1	SPEC. P.O.2	SPEC. P.O.3	ALT. T.C.	ALT. T.V.
0125					
0225					
0325					
0425					

	THR. TABLES	AERO. TABLES	GUID. TABLES	EX. TABLES	
0130					
0230					
0330					
0430					

EXTRA INPUTS

0000 (A)					

(A) : ALWAYS KEYPUNCH THIS CARD

```
SUBROUTINE SECT4
CALL
CALL
CALL

CALL
CALL
CALL

RETURN
END
```

```
SUBROUTINE SECT1
CALL
CALL
CALL

CALL
CALL
CALL

RETURN
END

SUBROUTINE SECT2
CALL
CALL
CALL

CALL
CALL
CALL

RETURN
END

SUBROUTINE SECT3
CALL
CALL
CALL

CALL
CALL
CALL

RETURN
END
```